D1517745

A True Novel

The Undoing

The uncertain nights of the Peterson children

Gloria Watson

Gloria Watson
Clovis, CA
www.biteword.com

This memoir is based on my experiences and family lore over an 18-year period. Some events are an imaginative re-creation based on family lore, others are based on my personal experiences and observations. The characters portrayed here are real, whether perpetrator or victim. In the case of incidental characters, all names have been changed, any resemblance to person living or deceased is unintentional.

Book Layout © 2014 BookDesignTemplates.com

The Undoing/ Gloria Watson.
ISBN 978-0-9862787-1-6

To my siblings,
We deserve to live in the light.

Acknowledgements

This book was completed with the love and support of my family and friends.

To that end, I am very grateful for the support of friends and family members who supported me via my RocketHub project. My thanks go out to my friends Matt and Paula Perelstein, Ed Newbegin, Richard Krauth, and Erika Friedman, and to my family Thelma Watson, Saurina Beach, Saundra Brucker, and Sharon Wireman.

In addition to financial support, there are those in this group that continue to provide other support so that I can reach for my dream. To my readers, Matt and Paula, Saurina, and Michele Soplata, I cannot thank you enough for the feedback that help me decide where changes were needed to help me move forward. Thanks to my daughter, Saundra, who is providing her technical skills to get my website and blog going. Most of all, a great big thank you to Richard Krauth, who for many years has mentored me and pulled me along. You have never wavered in your support for me every step of the way. I am forever grateful for your willingness to provide feedback and insight on this journey.

CONTENTS

Prologue

It all comes back to shame; no matter how angry, afraid, or hurt I felt, underneath every layer of pain, there was shame. My name is Gloria Peterson-Watson, and I am going to tell the story that is forbidden.

My father, George Allen Peterson Senior (Bud), was a psychopath with the traits of a sexual sadist. He had no capacity for love and failed to form attachments with any of his children. He had no remorse about the things he did. Nevertheless, he made sure that each of us was under his control enough that he would never face the consequences of the things he had done.

My original family was comprised of five children, one mother, and one father. This story tells of the early lives of the five children in my family. My oldest brother, George, was seventeen years old when it was over; my second brother, Richard (Dick), was sixteen. My sisters and I lived in that tortured place until Susan, Sharon, and I were eleven, four, and nine, respectively.

Our father came from a family very similar to ours with a loving mother and a vicious and abusive father. He was of above-average intelligence and was a master manipulator and liar. He was also completely detached and lacked empathy. He frequently sought stimuli to relieve his boredom or anger at someone else's expense.

At these times, he would look to his five children for entertainment and the "training" would begin. The sessions would always begin the same way—with one or two children as the

focus of his attentions and the others forced into the role of spectators.

Some people believe that psychopathy is hereditary; my own experience tells me that this is untrue. I believe that living with a sexually sadistic psychopath can create psychopathy if those exposed to the violence are desensitized to it. Not all children of psychopaths will assume their abuser's role. Some of us are survivors and live to tell about it.

I am a survivor of a psychopathic father. I have created a picture from my point of view. Every day was a challenge, every night was, well, you will see . . .

{ 1 }

The Petersons

Most people believe that they would know crazy on sight. It is not that simple; a psychopath is manipulative and very convincing. There are types of crazy hidden until it is too late. The Peterson children could sense crazy and know when it was coming. We would also try to escape it, in vain.

I have heard only stories about what happened before I was born. I will tell you the stories I have heard and been able to ascertain as fact. Exacerbating the issue is the fact that there is very little data about the women in the Peterson family.

I have only been able to find a few records regarding my Grandma Peterson, a very kind and loving woman who was an important part of my early life. I know that she had a sister named Etta. Etta lived with my grandmother after my grandfather passed away in 1954.

I have found records of births with no record of a subsequent death or life, for that matter. It is as if females were unimportant in the Peterson family. We will never know some of the details because secrets have been the stock and trade of the Petersons for generations. It could be potentially fatal to tell those secrets.

{ 2 }

The Grandparents

Our father's family consisted of five people: George Peterson I (father), Grace M. Peterson (mother), Marion (older brother), Marjorie (sister), and my sperm-donor father, George Allen Peterson Jr. (Bud).

By 1920, Grandpa Peterson had relocated to Hammond, Indiana. For a period, he and his brother Elmer lived with the Cobb family on Hickory Street. Grandpa was a soldier and his brother worked for the railroad.

When Grandpa left the Army, he met and married my grandmother, Grace, in 1921. The family owned a small home, a duplex in Hammond with one unit in the front occupied by the family and one unit in the back occupied by renters. Grandpa worked as a drafter in a machine shop.

By 1930, the couple had three children, ages seven, five, and three. The youngest was a girl named Marjorie (Pete). The oldest boy, Marion, was born in 1922, and the middle child was my father, Bud, born in 1924. Life in the Peterson home seemed normal by all outward appearances; the boys expected to excel both academically and socially and worked hard at meeting that expectation. In those days, the local

newspapers acted as everyone's social media; all activities were reported in the local newspaper. Even details about a trip to the museum were reported, often including information about who sat next to whom in the car on the way to the outing.

Both Marion and Bud participated in the Boy Scouts and book clubs. On occasion, both boys received academic awards. By all outward appearance, this was a normal, happy family of better-than-average achievers. However, there are no records of Marjorie receiving any academic or social achievements.

Nights at the Peterson house were a different story. The carefully controlled social facade constructed for public consumption fell away when George Senior arrived at home drunk. Alcohol lowered his tolerance for his wife and children; he often took it out on his family, sparing his wrath for no one.

The oldest son, Marion, died at 25 years old. He had a hunched back and heart problems. It was the opinion of most family members that his defects were the result of the merciless beatings his mother endured at the hands of George Senior when she was pregnant, carrying him. It made sense that George Senior may have resented the pregnancy and felt forced to become a family man when Grace became pregnant.

Marion, despite his disabilities, began to work at 17, peddling papers for $2.40 per week. However, his health would not allow him to continue, and the brutal blows frequently

dealt by his father made matters worse. Eventually, the physical problems he had resulted in his death in 1947.

Once the children were born, George Senior changed his focus to taking out his frustrations on his three children. Relentless in his pursuit of control, he laid down the law to his family. Each of the kids were told what was expected of them and knew what would happen if those expectations were not met. Nevertheless, their father had even darker plans in mind. Perverse and in control, he exacted complete silence from his wife and children.

Recollections of those days came from an aunt on my mother's side; she would babysit my brothers occasionally when my family still lived in the apartment behind Grandpa and Grandma Peterson's home in Hammond, Indiana. She spoke of many nights when George Senior would begin beating Grace so badly that Bud would have to go break it up. My aunt was often there for several days until someone could drive her eighty miles back to her home in Culver. She could recall the sounds of those beatings frightening her and kept her awake nights. The memories of those nights Grandma Peterson and the kids took to their graves often have made us wonder if the terror they endured was as bad as ours.

The Peterson children were subjected to their own special nightmare.. Bud was capable of very brutal acts.

Many articles debate whether psychopathy is genetic or results from a lack of nurturing. Many believe that it is both. Someone can be a psychopath because of their genetics; bad nurturing can inflame that tendency. Imagine someone who is

genetically pre-disposed to psychopathy, who is then nurtured by a psychopath from birth to adulthood.

My mother remarried, and we had a dad who loved us and cared for us the way a father is meant to care. Our new dad was never abusive and has played the role of father from the day he walked into our lives.

Over time and with great guilt, Mom talked about what happened. When we spoke of it, she was only told enough to put to rest whatever doubts she may have had. We never wanted her to feel guilty or doubt that she had made the absolute right choice in getting us away from Bud Peterson. He was nothing more than a sperm donor, once he was forced to leave our home, he was truly nothing more.

{ 3 }

George Gets Hungry

Bud was tired of the brats. He had never wanted kids and now they had two. It was 1951 and the oldest, George, was now four and Dick was three. His wife, Sylvia, had been pregnant several more times. Fortunately, he thought, she had lost the baby both times.

They lived in a modest home in Hammond, Indiana, the city where his parents lived. The house was an old house with a basement to be used as a laundry room. You had to navigate a very narrow stairwell to get into the basement. The stairwell had no headroom, and Bud was too tall to descend the stairs without bumping his head several times. The house had two bedrooms and one bathroom, a big living room and a huge country-style kitchen. It was just outside of town and sat on about two acres, big enough to make Sylvia happy with her garden and canning to keep her busy.

Bud had wanted to move farther away from his parents. His father pressured him to stay closer to Hammond and his control. Sylvia was unhappy that she could not live closer to her family. Bud thought that seeing them every Sunday was good enough. Sylvia's family had a bad habit, in Bud's esti-

mation, of getting the entire damn family together for a huge Sunday dinner. It was a bit overwhelming for Bud who was from a small family; Sylvia's family had eight kids and God only knows how many grandkids. Bill and Nona, Sylvia's parents, think that family is the most important part of anyone's life after God and Jesus.

At least this place was an improvement over listening to his mother scream and cry during the frequent nights that his father beat and fucked her. His father had also begun to fuck his sister, Marge. Everyone in that household was under his father's thumb. They all did what they were told and kept the dark secrets. His father had fucked both he and his brother, Marion, until Bud was old enough to force him to stop. That only made his father even crueler to everyone.

When Bud decided to get married, his brother and sister had both begged him to help them get out too. Bud had no consideration for anyone in his family. They could not count on him to help at all. After all, it was his mother's fault that she allowed his abuse, instead of leaving the mean old bastard. When he and Sylvia had married, they wound up living in the rear apartment at his parent's home. It had been a nightmare living with his parents. Bud was relieved to get his family out of that house and away from the bastard. Now his sister Marge was dating Sylvia's brother, Blackie. It was a good chance for her to get out. Bud hoped she kept her mouth shut.

Bud did not understand kids and certainly did not care in the least if they ate, were warm, or were hurt. George was sit-

ting in the middle of the kitchen crying that he was hungry and wanted something to eat. Bud thought to himself, "I'll give him something to eat!" His wife was still sleeping after getting home from her job at three this morning. He had no idea what to do with George, whose younger brother was still sleeping.

It was obvious, even at four, that George had more than the usual amount of smarts. Sylvia had taken him to the local kindergarten, and they allowed him early registration after testing him. It helped keep him busy in the afternoons. However, that was not helping Bud now.

Bud thought again that he would give this brat something to eat; he was angry and getting fed up with George fast. He decided what he would feed George; he unzipped the front of his pants and began to pull his penis out. Suddenly, Bud had another idea. It would not be as much fun, although it would be more exciting. It would also get George's mother out of bed. He just needed to think it through for a few more minutes.

He walked over to the cabinet and pulled out a can from the top shelf. As he set the can on the countertop, he decided that he needed an escape route before he went any further. Looking around, Bud decided that he could go out the kitchen porch door quietly and still watch what was happening without being seen. He began to get excited at the prospect and began to set his plan in motion quickly.

He walked over to George and told the boy that he was going to feed him since he was so hungry. George looked at him

suspiciously; it was unlike his father to offer him anything, especially food. He saw the can in one of his father's hands and a spoon in the other. "Come on, open your mouth!" Bud told the boy in hushed tones. George closed his mouth shut tight and shook his head back and forth. Bud tried several times to get George to open his mouth without luck. He needed to get the crystals in George's mouth; soon he was becoming very excited. He wanted to get it done and get to a place where he could watch and enjoy himself.

Bud sat the can on the floor. He used his free hand to hold George by the jaw and pressed the edge of the spoon against George's lips. As the crystals were exposed to George's lips, he screamed out at the caustic effect of the Drano. George's mouth came open as he screamed, and a small amount of the Drano fell on the inside of his lip, causing George to scream even louder.

The first scream startled Bud; he was not expecting such an immediate reaction from the Drano, and he missed the opportunity to slip the spoon into George's mouth even farther. He released his grip on the spoon, and it fell into George's lap. The Drano on George's legs began to burn as well. Bud walked quickly over to the porch door and slipped it open quietly. He stepped outside and then waited for his wife to come running at the sound of George's cries that were now full on screaming.

Bud looked back and saw George brushing the Drano off his lips and spitting it out. Bud could see that the kid was in great pain; Bud's penis was rock hard with excitement. He

grabbed his penis and began to jerk off watching the boy in pain.

Sylvia ran into the room and over to her son. She saw that he was struggling to get something out of his mouth and that he had burns on his chin. She gasped as she realized the can of Drano was on the floor. Sylvia grabbed George from the floor, took him to the sink, then began to rinse his face and mouth with water. "Spit it out, baby! Spit it out!" she cried as she tried to stop the pain and make sure that none of the Drano had gone down his throat. She was frantic and screamed Bud's name as she looked for her car keys. George was crying now but had stopped screaming. He kept saying, "I hurt, I hurt so bad Mommy."

Sylvia's heart was breaking for her son; she knew how badly Drano could hurt a child. That was why she had put the Drano up on the highest shelf; she had been sure that George and Dick would never be able to reach it. She pulled herself together, telling herself that there would be time to break down later; George needed to go to the hospital right now. She could see that his burns needed treatment and that no home remedy was going to work.

She yelled for Bud again and was surprised when he replied from the back door. "What the hell is going on here?" Bud said as he entered the back door. He was zipping up his pants; Sylvia thought for a moment that it was strange. The thought was fleeting, however; she had bigger fish to fry now.

Sylvia told Bud, "I have to take George to the hospital; you are going to have to watch Dick. I will return when I can. I will call you if there is any news."

"Christ! How did you let this happen? You could have killed the boy!" Bud told his wife. She told Bud to get rid of the Drano and not to buy any more to keep in the house. Sylvia turned and walked out of the kitchen to the door and heard Bud say, "We will discuss this when you get back," as she walked away. Sylvia was sure that there was a veiled threat in there somewhere. She was too tired and concerned about her son to care.

When Sylvia arrived at the emergency room, she carried George to the admitting desk. She told the admitting nurse what had happened. The nurse called someone on the telephone and people began to rush toward her. A doctor grabbed George from her arms and told someone to get a gurney. He immediately began to examine the burns on George's chin, lips, and tongue. He looked down his throat with a light and said, "It looks like the damage is limited to the mouth and chin." He looked at Sylvia and said, "Do you know how this happened?" Sylvia told the doctor that George climbed up to a high cabinet and got the Drano down by himself. George looked at his mother and wanted to tell her what had happened but was too afraid.

The doctor said, "I have seen way too many of these, but you are very lucky. As far as I can see, nothing went down his throat. If it had, he would be dying. We will have to keep him for a few days to be sure." Sylvia began to cry. She had been

so afraid that the worst had happened. The doctor comforted her and told her that she had done exactly the right thing getting him here so quickly. She picked up her little boy and cuddled him, telling him she was sorry he had been hurt. She would make sure that Drano was never kept in the house again. "Right now," the doctor said, taking George from her arms, "we need to treat those burns on his chin to make sure they don't get infected and stop them from hurting."

Turning to the nurse, the doctor said, "Bring me some topical ointment, bandages, and some Lidocaine; let's get that mouth numbed up and stop the pain." Sylvia thanked the doctor and waited until George was asleep before she left, promising him that she would be back in the morning.

Sylvia left the hospital feeling apprehensive. She could not reconcile herself to just how George had gotten into the Drano. Yes, he was a good climber, but they had discussed it. George understood the dangers of putting things like Drano in his mouth. She was left with only two possible conclusions, and she had been mulling both over in the hours she was at the hospital.

The first conclusion was that someone had put the Drano down on the floor intentionally; no one but Bud could have possibly done it. Dick was not awake when the whole thing began. That left Bud, and the thought was horrifying. The second conclusion she had come to was equally disturbing; that George had put the Drano in his mouth himself. He was too smart not to understand what might happen and that would mean he had intentionally meant to harm himself. Sylvia

shuddered at the thought—never; never would she believe George had tried to commit suicide.

When she arrived home, Bud was infuriated. Not only was food not ready for his dinner, but she was going to miss work; that meant less money for Bud. She gave him the news from the hospital. He told her to get his mother to stay with them and take care of the boys so that she would not lose any more work. She asked Bud if he had put the Drano down where George could get to it, and he stormed from the room shouting that it was her fault not his. He said that he would not listen to any more lies.

{ 4 }

My Family

Sometime before 1947, my parents met and married. I know this because my parents are not listed as a household on the 1940 census, and my oldest brother George was born in 1947. In 1949, my second brother, Richard "Dick," was born. During that time, my parents lived in either Hammond, Indiana or Gary, Indiana.

In 1953, Susan, my oldest sister was born. I was born in 1955, and my youngest sister, Sharon was born in 1960. There was another daughter born in 1957. That baby girl was listed in the Hammond Times as having been discharged home from the hospital with her parents, Mr. and Mrs. Geo A. Peterson. There is no further record of her birth or her death. I know that Mom gave birth to a baby that was stillborn in 1967 when I was twelve years old.

My mother told me herself that she had been pregnant ten times. My mother was not one to talk about difficult things. That makes seven out of ten pregnancies accounted for; what became of the other three children, I am not sure. It seems that they were probably stillbirths or miscarriages given the high infant mortality rate of the time. My mother's daughter born in

1957 remains a mystery; most children that were born and sent home from the hospital are listed in the vital statistics. If the infant later dies, they will be listed in the death index or cemetery rolls. It is because of my father's activities in relation to his children over the years that I find this suspicious. That baby girl simply disappeared.

{ 5 }

The Christmas Party

Susie and Gloria stood on the street holding hands. It was two days before Christmas and frigid. They stood in the dark in front of the steelworker's union hall where their father had dropped them off early that day. Now as the girls huddled together to avoid the cold, the union hall was empty and their father was nowhere in sight. The one-story building was made of red brick and had steel bars on the windows. When the girls had tried to return to the hall, they found the doors locked. The building had no exterior lights, so the atmosphere on the street was scary for the two small girls.

The union had held a Christmas party for the children of the local union members, and the turnout had been great. The girls had never seen so many Christmas goodies in their life; belonging to a large family, there was usually just enough to go around. The girls had never experienced such abundance. Each girl held a bag full of oranges, walnuts, and candy. Each girl had also been given a small toy. Susie, five, held her doll, still in the box, as she struggled to hang onto everything and keep her little sister, three, in tow hanging onto the small stuffed toy she received.

She was the big sister; it was her job to look after Gloria. If she lost her sister, her father would be furious. Susie had already seen just how mad he could get. When he got angry, he could hurt her really bad. Susie already suspected that their Daddy sometimes pretended to be mad just so he could yell at them and hit them. When he started acting that way, there was no telling what might happen before it was all over. Susie and Gloria did not understand it but just figured that everyone's Daddy was that way.

Gloria began to cry, asking Susie, "Why is it so dark? Where is Daddy?" Susie was as scared as her sister was and could not come up with an answer that would soothe the small girl. Gloria clung closer to her sister, and Susie tried to quiet her crying; it would be a bad thing if their father came and saw her crying. He would smack Susie for sure.

When a car pulled up, both girls pulled back from the curb and tried to hide in the shadows. The car was black and white with lights on top. Susie told Gloria it was a police car. One of the police officers got out and came over to the girls while his partner shined the spotlight on them. "Where are your mom and dad?" he asked the girls.

Susie told the police officer, "Our dad dropped us off today when it was still light outside; he will be here later to pick us up." The officer shook his head and told the girls that it was too cold and not safe for two little girls to be out on the street alone. When he asked the girls their names, the older girl replied, "Susie and Gloria."

"What is your last name?" the officer asked.

Gloria looked at Susie and waited for her to answer, Gloria did not know what a last name was. She was always called Gloria or "magpie" by her brothers and some of the cousins. She asked Susie, "Does he mean magpie?"

Susie shook her head at her sister and told the police officer "Peterson." The officer asked the girls how old they were, and Susie told the police officer, "I am five and she is three." The police officer asked the girls if they would like to get in the police car. The girls both shook their head, and Susie told the police officer, "We will get into trouble if our daddy comes to get us and we are not here." The officer looked annoyed and asked the girls if he could call their mother. Susie told the officer that their mommy was at work; there was no telephone number to call her with. When the officer asked where their mommy worked, Susie told him, "at a restaurant."

The officers decided to wait for another ten minutes to see if the father showed up and talked the girls into getting into the backseat of their police car to stay warm. He told them that it was okay because they were police officers and little girls could always trust police officers. When ten minutes had passed, the officers radioed the station. They were told to bring the girls to the station. Along the way, the officer was able to get the name of an aunt and uncle from the two girls. The girls knew that their Aunt Kitty and Uncle Rollie would come and get them. The girls also knew that their aunt and uncle lived in Culver, Indiana, right next door to their grandparents' house. The officers asked them what where their

grandparents names. When both girls replied "Grandma and Grandpa Crider," the officers laughed and asked if they were their mom's parents or their dad's. The girls both looked at the policemen and said, "I don't know, they are our grandparents." They both laughed at the young girls and told them that they had everything they needed to find them.

At the station house, the desk sergeant called the police station in Knox, Indiana, a small town close to Culver (which was even smaller, too small to have its own police station) and asked them if they knew of a family named Crider. They were told that the family was well known in the area and wanted to know if they had any first names. "Rollie and Kitty" was the response, and the police in Knox knew exactly who they needed. They told the Gary police officer that Rollie was one of two Crider brothers who owned the largest auto body shop in Starke County. When the Knox police found out what the situation was, they dispatched a car to the Crider's home and radioed back that Rollie and Kitty were on their way to pick up the girls at the Gary police station.

When the girls' aunt and uncle arrived, they found the girls sitting in the room where all of the officers were; the girls were being treated to hot chocolate and cookies. One of the police officers called his wife, and both of the girls were being showered with Christmas cheer. Rollie and Kitty asked the girls where their dad was and neither girl could answer. The girls told them that their dad had dropped them off at a Christmas party. The policeman told them that the girls had been found standing on the street in front of the steelworkers

union hall where a party had been given that day for the children of union members.

Kitty and Rollie looked at each other and told the police officer that Sylvia's husband, Bud, was not a member of any local unions. The policeman thought it strange but not a crime. Gloria piped up and told them all that their daddy left them at the party because "there was going to be no Christmas at home because they were rotten children and didn't deserve a Christmas."

Rollie and Kitty took the girls to their house in Gary; they had just driven eighty miles and still had to drive home. They were confused when they pulled up to a dark house. Kitty told Rollie to drive to the place where Sylvia worked and let her know that they had the girls. Rollie told Kitty, "Let's look around first to see if anyone is here." The two of them got out of the car and told the girls to wait there for them.

When the two walked up to the front door, it was unlocked, not unusual for folks living in the country, but Gary was full of crime and most people kept their doors locked tight. Rollie and Kitty walked inside and were dismayed to find no sign of Christmas in the house. There was no Christmas tree, no decorations, and not one gift was to be seen anywhere. The two of them walked back to the car in silence. They got back in the car and proceeded to drive to where Sylvia worked nights as a bartender until two in the morning.

When they arrived at the restaurant and bar, Kitty remained in the car with the girls while Rollie went inside to talk to Sylvia. Shortly, Rollie returned to the car with Sylvia

in tow. When Sylvia asked the girls where their dad was, the girls just stared at her in silence; they thought that their mommy would know, and the girls were becoming very upset.

They had fun all day at the party until the people working at the party told them they needed to leave and wait outside for their father. They had great fun getting so much attention at the police station despite the fact that their father had told them NEVER to talk to any police officers. Now, they were afraid again. "What if he is waiting at the party for us?" Susie asked.

Gloria said, "He will be so mad," and started to cry softly, trying to hide her face from the adults.

Sylvia wondered aloud, "Exactly why would Bud have just dropped the girls off at a union party when he was not a member and then never return for them?" Ever since he had lost his job and started drinking heavily, there was no telling what he would do. *My girls might have disappeared with no trace and I would have had no idea what had happened*, she thought to herself. Sylvia had no choice but to work nights so that she could take care of the kids once they returned from school each day. She was the sole support for the entire family at present.

Aunt Kitty and Sylvia were best friends; Aunt Kitty asked her about the fact that there was no Christmas tree or any other sign of Christmas at the house. Sylvia told Kitty that she would be unable to buy anything at all until the last minute as Bud had been drinking and not working for months. Kitty suggested that she and Rollie pick up the boys the next morn-

ing. They would take the girls back to their house for the night after picking up pajamas and some clothes for the next day. The girls, boys, and Sylvia could spend Christmas with them and worry about the details later. Sylvia cried and thanked her brother and sister-in-law, apologizing for the trouble they had already gone through to help her girls.

As Rollie and Kitty got back into the car with the girls, Sylvia returned to work. Kitty said aloud, more to herself than anyone else, "I thought I was done shopping. I guess I'd better get going early tomorrow."

Rollie said to her, "You can leave the girls with me and Blackie at the body shop tomorrow; that way we will have a chance to talk to them." Kitty looked at her husband and her heart swelled. *He is such a good man*, she thought.

Kitty wondered about Bud, Sylvia's husband, and Marge, Blackie's wife. Bud and Marge Peterson were brother and sister; both had such volatile moods and both had married into the Crider family. They had such different upbringings and now between the two couples had seven children. She knew that there was something different about the two of them, but no one could quite put their finger on what it was. She worried about her sister-in-law and best friend Sylvia; she was a Crider through and through, hardworking, honest, and loving. However, Sylvia was strong and would face up to whatever troubles came her way.

Two days later, Susie, Gloria, George, and Dick woke up at their Aunt Kitty and Uncle Rollie's house for Christmas morning. They joined their cousin May in the fest of holiday

gifts under the tree. May and Susie both received Barbie dolls and a Candy Land game. Gloria received an Etch A Sketch and a Cootie game. The boys received BB guns and new jeans. There were crayons and coloring books, card games and puzzles for the girls. Everyone was happy. It felt good; no one was yelling and hitting anyone. Gloria always felt safe and happy with her Aunt Kitty; she was one of the most loving and kind people that Gloria had ever know in her short life.

Christmas dinner began shortly after noon at Grandma and Grandpa Crider's house next door. The whole Crider clan was there and everyone had pitched in and helped. There was turkey, ham, rabbit, and chicken with all the trimmings. For dessert, there were six types of pies, whipped cream, eggnog, cookies, cakes, and Jell-O with marshmallows in it. There were cousins, aunts, and uncles everywhere, and except for the celebration of Christ's birth and so many pies, it was like any Sunday at the Crider farm. Afterward, the kids played and the adults rested. No one really noticed when Bud arrived, but he was suddenly there with the whole crowd and no one mentioned the trouble; it was Christmas after all, and he had brought along his widowed mother, Grace, and her sister Etta.

The Crider family believed that you did not discuss family issues in public and that Sylvia would have to deal with her husband in her own way and time. The Peterson children all wandered over to their Grandma Peterson (Grace) and greeted her with a hug and love. She was very special to Bud's kids, and they loved her a great deal. Grace did not have a mean

bone in her body. Everyone (except the youngest children) knew that some of those kind and gentle bones had been broken by her late husband. It was never spoken of; that was Grace's shame to bear and no one would embarrass her by bringing it up.

{ 6 }

One Too Many

This was Sylvia's eighth pregnancy. Two of the pregnancies had resulted in stillbirths between the second child, Dick, and the fifth pregnancy that produced the first girl, Susan, in 1953. Since then Sylvia had only been able to produce girls, Bud thought.

In 1955 after the second girl, Gloria, was born, Bud had decided that was enough. He told Sylvia to do something to prevent any further pregnancies. When Sylvia became pregnant again in 1956, he told her to get an abortion. Sylvia had refused, telling him that she believed abortion was wrong. She told Bud if he did not want her to get pregnant again, then they should just not have sex. Bud reacted by telling her that having sex was his right as her husband and her duty as his wife. He told her that he would have sex anytime he wanted it and that she could not stop him. Sylvia seemed to have few choices, but Sylvia warned him that if he did not behave, she would let her brothers know what he did. "Then," she said, "you can deal with them; they will not stand for you hurting me."

In March of 1957, when Sylvia had another baby girl, she was well aware that she was facing a challenge. At least Bud was working and spent little time at home, going to a bar to "kill time" before he had to come home. Often, he was so late that he missed dinner entirely, and Sylvia would put it in the oven for him to eat when he got home. He rarely did eat after he got home; she would find the food where she left it the night before. During those weeks, Sylvia was so tired that she would be exhausted each night when her head hit the pillow. She only woke if the baby fussed and she needed to take care of her.

It was clear to Sylvia that Bud would be of no help to her; he was avoiding being at home and had not even held the new baby. She had the distinct impression that he found this child completely unwelcome. She could not imagine feeling that way about a child of her own, but men are different from women and so she excused Bud's attitude. Bud was increasingly unhappy and created problems when he was at home. The kids really seemed much happier and more relaxed when he was gone. Sylvia tried to talk to George about it, but he just waved her away saying that nothing was wrong.

Life seemed a bit abnormal to Sylvia, but she could not quite define the source of the feeling. She kept trying to prevent anyone from seeing that things in her marriage were less than "normal." She confided about her doubts to her sister-in-law Kittie but no one else. She was afraid that news might get back to her parents, or Bud's, and she did not need the added pressure.

Bud's arguments were becoming more tiresome than caring for an infant. She was glad to have another baby but was determined not to have sex with Bud. She feared that another pregnancy might push Bud too far, yet he insisted on having sex. Sylvia was trying to be careful, monitoring her cycle and avoiding Bud on days when the risk of pregnancy was high. At twenty-nine years old, she was beginning to feel the strain of too many children and too little support. Still, Bud would argue with her to get her to have sex when she refused. The only way she could get him to stop was to tell him that she was at the highest risk of pregnancy in her cycle.

One night, she had gone to bed early, before Bud came home from the bar and tried to start another argument. The new baby was only three months old and yet was sleeping through the night, unless she was disturbed by a loud noise or a dirty diaper.

That night as she slept soundly in her bed, Bud slipped into the house as quietly as he could. He was not drunk; he knew that to pull this off and get away with it, he would need to be sharp.

He crept into their bedroom and over to the crib; he and Sylvia's bed was against the far wall. Bud could see that Sylvia was sound asleep and he stood there silently watching her sleeping for a bit. Once he was sure that Sylvia was not going to wake up during what he was planning, he returned his full attention to the crib. He stood for a few minutes looking at the infant who was as asleep as her mother was.

He leaned over the crib; he placed his right thumb and index finger over the baby's nose and squeezed it shut. Immediately, the baby's mouth popped open so that she could breathe. Bud had not expected that, but he quickly put the heel of his hand under the baby's chin and held it shut. He did not need to use much strength with the tiny girl; she waved her arms and legs a bit, not strong enough or big enough to put up a struggle. Bud watched in fascination as the baby slowly stopped struggling and became blue. She was gone, but her body was still warm. Bud had not considered this; his plan had been to wake up his wife and tell her he found the baby dead when he arrived home and checked on her. *This will actually work out better*, he thought, *Sylvia has been complaining that I never hold the baby or touch her in any way.* He decided to leave the baby as it was and let Sylvia find it when she woke up.

Bud undressed and climbed into bed carefully; he did not want to wake Sylvia before the baby was completely cold. He tried to sleep with a smile on his face. He found what he had done somewhat exciting and wished he could wake up his wife and force her to fuck him. However, this was almost as good as sex; he smiled again and drifted off to sleep.

Bud woke to Sylvia's scream; she stopped and walked over to the bed and bent over him. She was holding the baby and told Bud to get up and call the ambulance; she told him that the baby was dead. Bud grumbled that he was still sleeping. He asked her if calling the ambulance was going to change anything, and weeping, she told him it was too late.

Bud sat up in bed and, knowingly, began to comfort Sylvia, all the while feeding the fear that she was feeling. "What do you plan to tell the kids?" he asked. "Maybe we should call the police or take the baby to the hospital. What happened?" He took the baby from Sylvia's arms and said, "This baby is stone cold, what did you do? Did you forget to feed it or did you drop it?" Sylvia sat looking at him in shock. She told him that the kids were still asleep. "What do you want to do?" Bud asked. Sylvia said that she would just take the baby to the hospital. She told him she had heard that sometimes babies just quit breathing; this is what she thought had happened to the baby.

Bud asked Sylvia if she would like him to take the baby to the hospital before the kids woke up. "Yes," she replied, "I don't want the kids to know what happened. I will figure out what to tell them later." She was grateful to Bud for handling this; she was too upset to drive to the hospital and was not ready for the questions that she would have to answer there.

Bud watched as Sylvia wrapped the tiny baby in a fresh diaper and pajamas. She took a blanket and a quilt from the crib and bundled the baby up as if there was a snowstorm outside. Bud has seen her wrap up their kids just this way when they were small and the weather was icy. "Why are you bothering?" Bud asked her. "It isn't going to need any of those things, much less the diaper."

Sylvia began to cry again and said, "I just can't bear the idea of the baby getting cold on the way to the hospital. She is already so cold." He asked Sylvia if she wanted the clothes

and blankets back, which started a new spate of weeping. "No," she said.

Bud slipped the bundle under his jacket and headed out to the car. *How am I going to explain this? Maybe I won't,* he thought, *Sylvia will never bring this up again. People are used to young babies dying. I can just dispose of it and then tell Sylvia the hospital kept it.* Bud put the bundle in his trunk and stopped at the bottle store to pick up some bourbon; he was going to need fortification to get through this.

Bud drove around awhile, trying figure out where to dispose of his bundle. He couldn't go home too soon or Sylvia would be suspicious. Bud drank his bourbon and thought about his task while he was driving. He knew he couldn't go to his parent's home in Hammond because the yard was very small, and there wasn't a good place to dig a hole for it. He also couldn't go home because the kids would see him and become too curious.

Bud decided that the best place for him to take care of this and avoid detection was to go to his in-laws' property. He would bury it deep enough in the woods it wouldn't be disturbed or found. He approached the rural Culver, Indiana farm from the back to avoid being seen by any family members. He kept a shovel in his trunk and now retrieved that and the bundle after he parked. He began to walk and was thinking ahead to the time he would have to tell Sylvia what had happened.

He had to walk into the woods deep. His in-laws' farm started along the road that ran behind the property. The Crider's woods had fifty-five acres just in woods alone, and

that extended one-half the way across the property. Bud felt sure that he wouldn't be seen. He stopped about a quarter mile into the woods. He stopped and looked all around, making sure no one would be able to detect him through the trees. The woods were posted "No Hunting" so he was not worried that he might run into hunters other than his in-laws who owned the property. He decided that this would be the best spot and dropped the bundle to the ground. He laughed to himself as he recalled Sylvia bundling up the dead baby. She was so distraught she couldn't even think straight.

He began digging a hole wider than he needed. In order to go deep enough to prevent animals from digging the infant up, he would need the extra room to dig deeper at the bottom of the hole. It was thirsty work for June, so he stopped to rest and drink from his bottle occasionally. He was really feeling buzzed. In the beginning, he thought it was the alcohol; soon, he realized that the buzz he was feeling was greater than just alcohol. He actually felt very powerful; he was excited and could feel his cock hardening. He decided to stop digging; the hole was deep enough for that bundle.

Bud took the quilt off the bundle and sat down on it atop a nearby log. He unzipped his pants and began to rub his cock as he took another drink. It felt good, but he thought there was something more driving the pulsing feeling he had. He was glad he was so far into the woods and very alone. He laughed again as he remembered Sylvia dressing the cold, blue infant, and he took the receiving blanket from around it and set it next to him. He then stood over the hole, took off the infant's

cleaned himself off. He wondered why he was not at all disgusted by what he had done. He would like to tell Sylvia every detail so he could force her to have sex afterward, but he knew that she would not keep quiet.

He drove home, sated and powerful, thinking of what he would tell his wife about what had happened at the hospital. He felt that if he just pretended ignorance, she would quit questioning him. He grabbed his crotch and squeezed his balls; damn, he thought, this memory would be excellent for whacking off for a long time.

When he got home and Sylvia found a quiet moment when she could ask, he told her that the hospital had kept the body. He told her, "They told me it was not unusual for babies to stop breathing for some unknown cause and that they would take care of the body." Sylvia was upset and asked when the hospital or funeral home would call her to make arrangements. He was not prepared for the question and answered, "I don't know; sometime in the next few days, I imagine."

When Sylvia did not hear from the hospital or funeral home in a week, she called the hospital and asked what the disposition of the baby's body was. She told them she would like to have a funeral soon. They told her they did not have any unknown infant's bodies and that she should check with the coroner's office. Checking with the coroner had the same results. In fact, there was no record of the infant's death at all. Sylvia became concerned; she suspected that Bud had simply walked out of the hospital without waiting for any answers.

Unable to find any evidence that the baby had been in any of Hammond's hospitals, Sylvia tried to put it behind her and get on with life. She had a job and four kids to take care of and a husband who suddenly had begun to act rather odd, with a sense of entitlement he had never had before.

{ 7 }

Our House In Hebron

Sometime after 1955 when she was born, Gloria's parents moved from Gary, Indiana to a small rural town, Hebron, Indiana. The home in Hebron was a ten-acre farm not far from town. In 1960, Hebron was a small farming town with city limits of one and a half square miles and a population of around 3700 people. To reach the farm, you had to travel several miles south of town and make a right turn at Road 900 South, where the Hebron Cemetery still sits today. The small farm was the first home that Gloria could remember clearly; it consisted of ten acres with a modest home and a large yard that included a garden, an orchard, and a ring of black walnut trees. In the ring of trees, the family often had summer cookouts and campouts. The orchard was on the east side of the property, beyond the ring of trees; apples grew there along with some very large pigs. The house stood to the west of the farm, near the road, and beyond that, the garden and barns.

The neighbors to the east were long-time friends Vernon and Iola Wilson. They had three children, one of them an adopted nephew. The Wilsons ran a dairy farm and had chickens. Gloria enjoyed helping (if a four-year-old was much help

at all) skimming cream from the cans of milk and churning butter. They also worked as a team to clean chickens in the kitchen, and Gloria's job was to pluck the feathers from the dead chickens. As much as she disliked doing that, she was not going to gut them; she had too many beheaded chickens tossed her way as a small child. Gloria was not sure who screamed loudest, those poor chickens (before their heads were chopped off) or her.

Gloria recalled sitting in a high chair when she was younger, her mother handing her snacks to keep her busy while she prepared meals. As she got older, Gloria and her mother would sit out on the picnic table and shuck peas for dinner or take popcorn off the cob and then shake it to get rid of any excess husks. Gloria's mother had a storage shed in the backyard next to the garden where she kept her tools for gardening. She also kept items in that shed that she used for canning. Gloria was always in trouble for getting into that shed.

One day, Gloria found her way to the top of that shed. Only four years old, she had somehow managed to get up on the roof. Her mother was mad, and confounded. She was too scared to come down, so her mom got her brother George to get her down. Gloria's brother at twelve was already taller than their mother who stood all of four feet eleven inches tall. Gloria could not tell her that her father had put her on the shed and told her that she had to jump down.

Gloria's father had stood there watching her and egging her on to jump down. It was a tall shed to a very small four-

year-old. He told her that if she did not jump he would come up there and get her; then he said he would beat her until she was blistered all over. Gloria was too afraid to jump, knowing that, even if she did jump, he would still find a reason to hurt her. As Gloria stood there wondering what to do, her father suddenly stopped talking and walked away.

In the next few seconds, Gloria's mother discovered her on the shed roof. Gloria was relieved but still too frightened to come down. Knowing she had a beating coming either way, Gloria let George help her down.

Her mother repeated the story of how she found her on top of that shed often, telling everyone how "for the life of her" she couldn't figure out how Gloria had gotten up there. She told every relative and friend she saw. She also told everyone again during the next Sunday dinner at Grandpa and Grandma Crider's house in Culver. Gloria wanted to curl up in a ball and hide. Sometimes, when things were too much for her at the Crider family Sunday dinners, she would go hide in the woods that were behind their house. She never strayed too far, though; Gloria knew better than to cause any trouble.

Gloria's sister knew. Susie told her about the bad things that could happen if she got the attention of their father. Gloria would hear Susie cry sometimes when he came into their room at night. Their mom worked nights and did not get home until late. The girls' father told them that he could do anything he liked and their mother could not stop him. He also warned them that they were not to tell their mother anything or he would have to take her out back to the cutting block and cut

off her head just like the chickens. Gloria had nightmares of her mother flopping around on the ground looking for her head, asking Gloria to help her find it.

Susie told her that sometimes their brother Dick came into the room at night and made her touch him.

Gloria would lie awake in bed for hours waiting for her mother to come home from work and bring with her the feeling of safety so that she could sleep. Many nights, her parents would fight, yelling and screaming at one another. She always wanted to get out of bed and defend her mom; her father had no right to yell at her mother. But she was too afraid, too afraid to move, too afraid of what he might do if he knew she was awake.

It was in that year, when Gloria was four and her mom was working late, that her father began to have his "training sessions." Gloria was unsure how else to explain them. When Mom was at work, and if Dad was in a bad mood or just bored, he required their full attention and participation in his "experiments."

Since Gloria was still so young, some of the details of what happened to her brothers and sisters was foggy. However, she could recall those nights. She was always terrified he would force her to participate instead of just being a spectator, and eventually they all had to participate. It happened so many nights that only the most horrific sessions remained in her memories. Their father believed that his children were only put on this earth for his amusement.

Gloria recalled watching what was happening to one or more of her siblings and being so horrified that she would just shut down. Sometimes, he would notice that Gloria had gotten too quiet and would ask her if she wanted to try it out. Gloria would start to cry, and he would hit her for crying. She would stop crying, and the inevitable slap would come again along with a "what's the matter, didn't that hurt enough?" There was no way to avoid his ire; you were damned either way.

{ 8 }

Please Don't Leave Me

She could sense the tension. By the time Gloria was four years old, she knew when the house was on the verge of another crisis. She had been listening to the yelling late at night and the way her father threatened her mother. Late at night, Gloria would lie in bed terrified that her father, Bud, would carry out this threats against Sylvia, her mommy. Last night had been particularly scary, and Gloria could feel the anger seething from every pore in her father's body.

Since the bad things had begun, Gloria had gotten very good at slipping out of the house and hiding in the orchard or the walnut grove. The walnut trees had been planted in a circle, and on warm nights when Gloria crept out there to hide, she could lie on her back and look up at the night skies. The nights were often clear and the stars bright above the home they lived in; the real darkness dwelled within the home.

One afternoon, Gloria realized that her mommy was getting ready to leave the house and go out. She followed her mommy outside and quietly followed her to her car. She wanted to go with her mother; she was too afraid to stay with

her father. He was very angry, and Gloria was desperate not to be near when he exploded in rage; it always hurt too much.

Sylvia turned around as she realized that Gloria, her youngest, had followed her out to the car. "Go back inside," she told her little girl.

Gloria began to plead with her mother, "Please let me go. I promise I will be good. Please! Please! I can't stay here."

Sylvia said, "No, I need to go to the grocery store and you cannot come. Stay home with your dad."

Gloria's eyes opened wide and she grabbed her mommy's hand, pleading even harder, sensing that she was going to have to stay at home with her father. "Please don't make me stay here with him; please, please, please let me come with you. I am scared."

Sylvia looked at her little girl and wondered what had gotten into her. Gloria seemed deeply afraid of something, but Sylvia was exhausted. Working late nights at the restaurant and taking care of the house and kids was really beginning to get her down. Now she was pregnant again and her husband was acting like a complete ass. She looked down at Gloria and sighed. "No, sweetie, you cannot come this time. I promise to bring you some M&M's if you are a good girl. You don't need to be scared, honey."

Realizing she had lost, Gloria lay on the ground and began to sob. "I am so scared, mommy. Please don't go, don't leave." After a few moments, Gloria looked at her mommy and realized she had said too much. The look on her mother's face was one of fear and unhappiness. Gloria got up from the

ground and stopped crying. She told her mommy that she was okay, and it was all right for her to go to the store.

Sylvia was surprised at Gloria's immediate change of attitude, and she realized the girl was still afraid. Now, however, her own fear had changed because of Gloria's reassurances. Despite her doubts, Sylvia got into the car and left for the store. She told Gloria she would hurry back and promised her M&M's when she returned.

Gloria told her mommy that "it was okay" and "she really liked M&M's." Gloria was fearful that her father had heard what had just happened. She was even more afraid for her mommy now, even more than for herself. As she walked to the back of the house, Gloria sobbed, why had she let her mother go? She had sold out for M&M's! She lay down in the walnut grove and cried. She hoped her mommy got back soon; things were getting louder in the house already.

{ 9 }

All Wrung Out

As Sylvia's foot hit the bottom step of the neighbor's back porch, she heard the first scream. Her first thought was that the sound came from the orchard beyond her house; she quickened her pace only slightly.

She had been visiting her nearest neighbor and best friend, Iola. Sundays provided a break for her during the week from the relentless flow of housework, taking care of the kids, going to work at night, and fighting with Bud when she arrived home around 3:00 a.m. She enjoyed the walk through the walnut orchard between the houses; it was shady, cool, and gave her a few minutes to plan dinner before she got to the house and had to get back to the grind.

She was torn from her thoughts by more screams and broke into a run when she realized that the screams were coming from somewhere inside the house. Something was wrong; it sounded as though a wounded animal had somehow gotten into the house. Sylvia felt as though she were running through molasses. Every ounce of energy in her body was willing her to run faster, but something akin to dread made her feel as

though her body weighed far more than its ninety-three pounds.

As she grew closer, she realized that the screams were those of one of her daughters, and she could feel her lungs begin to burn as adrenaline surged through her system. "Oh my God," she thought, "that screaming!" As she heard the child plead in a keening scream, "Mommy, mommy, help me!" Sylvia understood it was Gloria who was in trouble. Sylvia said aloud to no one at all, "Oh God, what is wrong?" Her mind began to race with the possibilities of what could be happening as she ran up the rear steps to the house. Sylvia looked around for Bud, the kids' father, for help but did not see him anywhere. She pulled open the screen door and ran into the screams echoing throughout the house.

Bud stepped back into the shadows away from the window in the garden shed as Sylvia ran through the gate that separated the neighbor's property from their own. He had been listening to the screaming for several minutes and seeing the panic on his wife's face excited him. He rubbed himself through the front of his pants; he knew the kids could see, but he did not care. These kids knew better; they would keep their mouths shut.

He'd told Gloria not to scream; if she did, he would return and beat the hell out of her. He did not really think that a kid that small could scream so loud, but the girl was good and scared. He had created an impressive amount of fear when he clamped the roller arm down on the wringer washer. She had begun to scream almost as soon as the wringer had begun to

pull her fingers in. At first, he had made the other kids watch, but when the girl began to scream, he made the others go out to the garden shed so that he could shut her up. Once they left, she began to scream so loudly, he had to leave her there and hide in the shed himself. Before he left, he had turned to her and said, "You had better not tell, or else." He made a motion with his hands that the girl knew all too well for her young age and her eyes opened wide with terror. Bud laughed and walked out the door, joining his other children in the garden shed.

Bud had told the other three children not to leave the shed until he came and got them. As he joined them in the shed, Bud noticed that the children were sitting up in the window looking out. "Get the hell out of that window," Bud yelled at the children. "Do you want your mother to see you, dumb fucking stupid kids?" Bud hit the ten-year-old boy upside the head. "Move faster! Dumbass, you are in my way!" he yelled at the boy as he moved into position so he could watch to see when Sylvia would notice the girl was screaming and come running.

His excitement began to grow as he realized that this time, he might have injured a kid badly. Surely, he hadn't killed the girl; otherwise, it would be much quieter. He wondered if he had put the girl's right hand in the wringer or her left; dammit, he should have been sure to put the right hand in because of the aneurysm in her right wrist. It would have been more in-teresting if it burst; the doctors kept saying that it could at any

time. As Bud watched, his wife ran into the back door, and he slipped out of the shed to see what would happen next.

As soon as their father left the shed, two of the three children began to cry. Susan, the oldest girl at six, began to wail, "Gloria is dead, she is dead!"

Her oldest brother, George, who was twelve, was crying but calm and told her that if Gloria was dead, she wouldn't be screaming.

"That screaming is scary," said Dick, age ten. "I hope she stops soon or we are all gonna get it." Dick knew far too well that their father could get just as angry if you cried as if you did not.

George calmed the others down and told them, "Let's go in the house." The others knew this was not what they had been told, but George was the oldest and usually right, so they followed him into the house to see how Gloria was. George knew that once their mom was home there would be safety from whatever their father was up to because Mom did not work on Sunday. Tonight would be a refuge from the nightly uncertainty.

Gloria did not like this game; it was scarier than the other games her father liked to make them play. He was in a meaner than usual mood today, and he said the game was going to be for keeps.

Her father told her to stand in the tub for the wringer washer. At four, Gloria was small for her age and could not reach the top of the tub, so he picked her up and put her in the

tub. He told her to sit down on the tub rim so he could decide what to do next.

He spent a few minutes telling Gloria what she should say when her mother found her. He told her that no matter what, she was to tell her mother that she was "trying to help her with the washing" and that "she was sorry she had got herself hurt." Her mom would be mad, but no matter what, Gloria was not to tell her that her father had put her hand in the wringer; otherwise he would have to kill her and her mom. He may even have to kill all of them. He told her it did not matter to him either way; it was Gloria's decision. Live or die, tell or not. Gloria believed every word her father said.

As Bud held Gloria's fingers to the rollers of the wringer-washer, they would not be pulled into the rollers. Bud found that he had to push a towel through the rollers to get the process started. Gloria started to shake and said, "Please, Daddy, don't." Bud laughed at the girl as she began to cry. As the rollers began to pull Gloria's fingers in and gobble up her hand, fear gave way to terror, and Gloria uttered an earsplitting scream. Bud hit her on the ear and whispered, "Shut up!" only she could not help herself. The girl screamed and screamed again as her hand became her wrist. She could feel the rollers travel over the bump that the doctors had told her mom was her "yurism." She did not know what that was, although she did not think was good. Gloria became more frightened and more shrill as she watched the rollers grind along their crushing path. She screamed, "Somebody please help me" as she thought about her skin splitting and her bones

popping out. The young girl screamed again, "Please don't leave me here." She lost control of her bladder and began to squeal along with her now incoherent screams, creating an animalistic cacophony of frantic sound.

Suddenly, Gloria realized that she had been left alone; she began to try to unlatch the wringer arm in a desperate attempt to free herself. Because she was small for her age, Gloria could not reach the clasp. Her father had put her right arm through the wringer at the center of the rollers, making the distance farther than her left arm could reach. At that moment, the rollers grabbed her elbow, and the agony created by the force of her elbow passing through the rollers caused a fresh shout of pain from her as her head hit the wringer housing. Gloria watched in horror as her upper arm began to be pulled into the rollers. She began to scream again as she wondered what was going to happen if no help came before the rollers got to her shoulders, her neck, and finally her head. Gloria gave up screaming and weeping as she realized that there was no help, no hope. Someday, if not today, her father was going to win at the game.

Sylvia ran into the laundry room shortly after the scream-ing had stopped. She found her youngest daughter, Gloria, sitting in the wringer washer with her whole arm caught in the rollers all the way up to her armpit. "What are you doing in there; how did you get up there?" Sylvia said as she rushed over to the washer and unlatched the arm that held the rollers down.

Gloria began to wail as her mother put her down and told her mother: "I was trying to help you with the wash." "It was an accident." "Mommy, I hurt my yurism." "Mommy, I peed my pants." "Mommy, I am so scared." Gloria looked over her mother's shoulder and saw her father standing there. He was motioning with his hands as he had earlier before he left her alone in the laundry room. When Bud asked Gloria, "What are you afraid of?" she replied, "the washing machine." He told her "that would teach her to help with the wash." Sylvia looked at Gloria's hand, arm, and fingers and found that nothing at all was hurt. It appeared that even the aneurysm was intact. It nagged at Sylvia that she could not put together in her mind how Gloria had gotten into the washer and how she had latched the wringer rollers down but not been able to un-latch them to get loose.

Bud left the room in disgust. *All that screaming and the kid wasn't even the least bit hurt,"* he thought. *"I am going to have to get more creative,"* he said to himself. He had taken some risks to pull this off on a Sunday when Sylvia wasn't working; he thought it would have at least been worth it, but the rush had not lasted long. Now he was going to be stuck at home all night without any way to take it out on the kids.

Susan held her sister's hand as they left the laundry room and went to their bedroom. She helped her little sister change into dry clothes; they lay down and held each other. Both of the girls were shaking, one from fear and the other from the cold of the water and terror of what had just happened to her.

As Gloria's teeth chattered hard against each other, Susan rubbed her back to comfort her and slowly she began to quiet.

Both of the girls' brothers had retreated to their bedrooms and were playing quietly so not to disturb their father and make him angry.

Later, Sylvia brought the subject up to Bud and asked him what he thought about how the girl had gotten into that mess all by herself. He was defensive on the subject and told Sylvia that if she had something to say, she should come right out with it. Bud told her that she should just keep her fucking mouth shut if she didn't know what she was talking about. Bud told Sylvia, "That is what happens when you run off to the neighbors to visit when there is washing to get done."

Sylvia dropped the subject, puzzled by his reaction. He used the argument to storm out of the house and go for a drive. He had been drinking all day and decided that if he couldn't have fun at home, he might find opportunity for fun elsewhere.

Sylvia was glad to have Bud out of the house for a while. She was still trying to understand what had happened. This was not the first time that matters did not quite add up, and Sylvia was beginning to wonder what was happening to her family.

{ 10 }

Bud Hunts

Bud was very angry. Sylvia had insinuated that he had something to do with Gloria getting herself into the washer/wringer. That was a little too close for comfort.

Bud drove and his anger slowly abated. It was replaced with an itchy kind of restlessness and boredom that made him need to hurt someone.

He wanted booze, but Indiana was a dry state on Sunday, and he would have to drive all the way to Michigan to get more. He decided that he had nothing better to do and turned north on Route 2 then turned east on Route 30 and north on Highway 421 toward Michigan City and then east again to Route 12 to cross the border into Michigan. He also realized that once he was out of the rural, small towns between Hebron and Michigan City, he could find some action.

He began to see working girls along the streets outside the bars in Michigan City; the way they were dressed got his appetite up. Bud waited until he reached Michigan, that way he could have booze and women. He liked it that way.

Bud drove up and down West Buffalo Street, the main drag in New Buffalo, Michigan. After a bit, he spotted a

woman that was petite, like his wife, and who had the same dark hair even if she was dressed like the whore she was. He pulled alongside the road and rolled down his passenger window. When she approached, he asked her to give him a price for an hour and they negotiated. She opened the door and climbed into the car, and then she directed him to a small motel up the street where she felt safe.

Bud told her that they needed to make a stop at the bottle shop first so he kept driving past the motel. He also told her that he was looking for "car sex" if that was okay with her. Again, she agreed and Bud knew he had everything lined up to go his way.

After stopping at the bottle shop, Bud flipped the car around, away from the main drag, and headed out of town. He told her that he had a place in mind where they would not be disturbed. Once he found the place he had in mind, Bud pulled over. He drank from the bottle he had purchased and sat looking at the woman, trying to decide how to precede. The woman asked if he planned to offer her a drink from his bottle. Bud replied, "Why waste good booze on a whore?"

At that point, the woman, sensing his hatred, grabbed the door handle and realized it did not work. She yelled at Bud, "You'd better let me out of this car, right now." Bud laughed and leaned over and punched the woman in the face. "Go ahead and yell," he said, "no one will hear you out here."

Bud continued to pound on her and she kept crying out in pain. Bud looked at her and said, "You said your price was ten dollars for an hour, anything I wanted, so shut the fuck up.

You are giving me a headache." He punched her in the stomach and told her to get out of the car. He went around the car and opened her door so that she could get out. He pushed her forward into a field; there were no homes in sight, and it was too dark for anyone to see them. Each time she fell down, he would kick her with his construction boots until she got up and started moving forward again. When she fell, he would kick her in the crotch, hard. It made him feel powerful.

When they had gone far enough into the field, Bud told her to take off her clothes and lie down. She complied, and even though she had gone completely quiet, Bud kept telling her to shut up. She thought that maybe he was hearing voices in his head.

Bud looked at the woman; he thought that she was talking to him, degrading him for not being man enough. However, he realized that the voices were not female, they were male. He looked around and saw no one else anywhere. Too much booze, he laughed to himself and undid his pants, sliding them down past his knees.

The woman did not like his laugh; she was worried that she would not come out of this alive. She had had kinky customers before, but there was something seriously cruel and crazy about this one. She had decided to just be quiet and try to get back to town alive.

Bud looked down at the woman on the ground and mumbled that she could not even follow directions. He wanted her on her knees, face down. He kicked her leg and told her to turn over and get on her knees. As she complied, Bud thought,

"yes, just like a bitch." Bud knelt down behind her and shoved his cock into her, stroking a few times to get good and wet. She was not at all wet because she was so afraid. Bud pulled out, spit on his cock, and placed the end of his cock at her rectum.

Sensing what he had planned, the woman cried, "No, I don't do that!"

"Now you do," Bud replied as he laughed and shoved his cock into her ass as hard and fast as he could. He could feel her tearing and saw blood seeping out but laughed even harder and continued to ram himself into her ass. He laughed louder as she cried out more, begging him to stop. He really enjoyed the feeling of power over this bitch and once he came, considered raping her again. However, it was late and the longer his car sat alongside the road, the greater the risk of discovery.

As Bud cleaned himself, using her clothing, he said to her, "That is what you get for being such a dirty whore; thanks for the memories." He then delivered a blow to her chin that knocked her out as she tried to stand up. Bud decided that he needed to add one more touch and pissed on the unconscious woman as she lay there. He laughed, zipped up, and walked out of the field to his car and drove off, heading back toward Indiana, drinking from his bottle along the way.

{ 11 }

A Cold Shocker

Since the time he had tortured Gloria by placing her arm into the wringer, Bud had been giving a lot of thought to doing more work in the laundry room. It had several advantages that he had not previously perceived.

The laundry room for the house was built with drains in the floor and had linoleum that ran from the floor to thirty-six inches up the wall to prevent damage from water. In the room were two grey iron sinks that were square and very deep. One of the sinks had a drain board attached to it for cleaning produce and butchered meats during the canning and harvest seasons on their ten-acre farm. Sylvia used the laundry room to wash clothes, clean chickens after slaughter, and prepare fruits and vegetables for canning. The room was adjacent to the kitchen with a door that led directly to the back porch for muddy days.

Bud had been thinking that he could make good use of the iron sinks and drain board. The floor drains would come in handy if he "accidentally" made a mess. The wringer/washer was in the middle of the room but could be moved out of the way. This day, Bud took a car battery into the laundry room.

He hooked it up to a 12-volt battery charger and plugged the charger into an outlet close to one of the sinks. Sylvia asked him what he was doing with a battery and charger in the laundry room. She did not want the battery acid or the dirt and oil getting where she cleaned clothes and prepared foods. He told her that he would cleanup after himself and set down a pair of jumper cables next to the charger. "Now what do you need that for?" Sylvia asked him; she was tired of his attitude and was in a hurry to get out the door and to work. Bud had been barred from the restaurant where she worked by the owner who told her that if he came around again, he would have to fire her. Without the threat of him walking into her work, going to work was becoming a refuge to her. Bud told his wife that he wanted to keep everything together. Sylvia started to argue but decided against it and left for work.

Once Sylvia had gone, he placed three of the kitchen chairs in the laundry room facing the wall where the sinks were located. Then he sat down to think some more; he wanted this to be his best ever. Bud anticipated some real entertainment tonight; edgy and bored, he was looking for excitement. The kind of excitement that the bitch he was married to no longer provided. Sure she was okay in a pinch, but now that she was pregnant, she was moody and uninterested in sex.

He looked in the refrigerator to see if there was any ice in the freezer but found only one tray. He checked the freezer in the laundry and found a bit more, but still not enough to have the effect he wanted. Next, he took a couple of towels and laid them on the drain board. The kids were outside playing until

dark, and he thought that he could wait until they came in and still have plenty of time to get his work done. He sat down again to think through his plan. He wanted to create maximum effect but not have any visible damage occur. If it did, he would just keep going and see what happened. He could explain it away as he always did.

As the kids came inside, he had them sit down in the chairs he had placed in the laundry room. All but one; he had Susan stand up and wait until everything was ready.

Bud went over to the sink with the drain board and put in the plug. He turned the water on, using only the cold-water spigot. He stopped and thought for a minute. He looked at Susan and could see the terror in her eyes; she was six years old and average sized for her age. He told her to take off all of her clothing. She began to cry and take off her clothes. Bud pulled back his fist and told her to shut up. As she quieted down, he told Gloria to get up and come over. He then told Susan to sit down. Susan began to put back on her clothes, but Bud stopped her. Bud told Gloria to take off her clothes as well. As she took off her clothes, Bud went over and turned off the water at the laundry sink. Next, Bud plugged the other laundry sink and began to fill it with cold water as well.

At that moment, Bud grabbed Gloria up and placed her in the sink full of cold water. Gloria squealed at the effect of the cold water and tried to scramble out of the sink, but her father held her down by her shoulders. He told her, "If you try to climb out of the sink again, I will drown you in it." Gloria stopped struggling and cried quietly. Bud told her to "stop

sniveling, you haven't been hurt yet." Then, realizing that the other sink was full as well, he grabbed up Susan and placed her in the other sink. Susan had a similar reaction to the cold but knew better and sat down in the water quietly.

Bud was thinking that he wasn't done yet, not even close. He walked over to the battery charger that had been charging the car battery he had brought in earlier in the day. He turned off the charger and unplugged it. Next, he took the jumper cables and clamped one end onto the metal sink that Gloria sat in. He saw no reaction from Gloria and realized that he needed another set of cables to make a complete circuit. He had not planned well enough because he only had two sets of jumper cables but had two sinks full of little girls.

He hooked up the other battery cable completing the circuit, but still no reaction from Gloria. She seemed very drowsy now, and he wondered if the cold water was causing her to go into shock. He went over to the sink where Gloria was and put his hand into the sink. He immediately pulled his hand back as he felt the charge that was in the water. He also noticed that all of the areas where Gloria was in the water were swollen and above the water, no effect.

Swiftly, he grabbed Susan and placed her in the same sink as Gloria. "Ouch," Susan said and then quieted down.

"It tingles, huh?" Bud asked the girl. Susan nodded her head. She also appeared drowsy, and Bud began to watch the girls to see how much of an impact this water shocking was having on them. He noticed that Gloria seemed unconscious but still breathing now and Susan was dropping off as well.

{ 12 }

Pig Season

Sylvia could see her sister Bev headed her way with a determined look on her face; it was Sunday and as usual, all of the families were gathered at her parents' home in Culver, Indiana. "Sylvia," Bev said, "that girl of yours says the craziest things sometimes, and she is telling all of the other kids that she is going to die pretty soon. She told them that because the hog was killed that now she will die and pretty soon, too."

Sylvia sighed and looked at Beverly, her younger sister. Beverly was married to a nice man named Walter Pflugshaupt. Walter was a hog farmer; he worked hard and treated her sister and the kids great. Bev would never understand what it was like to be married to Bud Peterson because Bev had married well. Sylvia replied, "I know, I don't really understand what she is so upset about. Somehow she has gotten it into her head that the kids get killed along with the hogs during slaughter, but not all kids just her."

Sylvia did not want to recount for her sister the look on four-year-old Gloria's face when she found her hiding in the coat closet, the screaming when she had to pull her out, or the

absolute certainty of the girl that her father planned to put her on the trailer and take her to the butcher next.

As Bud sat the girl on the hog's back, he told her, "You stay on this hog until your mother comes to get you, or until the hog throws you off and eats you, whichever comes first." Bud turned and walked away from the orchard, laughing to himself at the fear in the girl's eyes as she was sat down on the pig.

The hog was really big and scary; it was the biggest pig on their ten-acre farm. Gloria looked at the hog and grabbed one of its ears, releasing it quickly when the hog squealed and started to run. Gloria was lying flat on the hog's back and trying to hang on by the neck. When it ran close to the barbed wire fence, she had not moved quickly enough and now her leg was bleeding. She was afraid the hog would smell the blood, become crazy hungry, and eat her as her father had said. Now, she was stuck on the back of the hog, being too far from the fence to climb off and too high to jump to the ground. Her father had left her there and warned her, "The day that we slaughter this hog is the day you will be strapped to the trailer and hauled off to be carved up into cracklings too."

When Gloria saw her father and the neighbors coming down the driveway of the ten-acre farm where the family lived, she was sure they were coming for her. She headed for the safest place she could think of, the winter coat closet. Still filled with the bulky snowsuits and galoshes from the recent

winter storms, Gloria knew that she could hide under a few of the coats with little trouble.

However, it wasn't long before she heard her mother calling her name. The longer her mother called, the more annoyed her voice sounded. Gloria was not afraid of her mother, at least not nearly as afraid as she was of her father. However, before long, Gloria heard the door open to the closet where she had found safety. "What are you doing in there?" her mother asked.

"I am not going to go to the butcher! I don't want to die like the hog!" she cried. Sylvia looked at her daughter and wondered why she thought she was going to be killed.

Sylvia thought that maybe it was because the girl seemed to have some sort of special relationship with the hog. In fact, she had found Gloria out in the orchard several times on the back of the creature. She had never been able to figure out how Gloria had managed to get on the back of the hog; it was huge and she was barely the size of a child half her age. Now, she seemed distraught that the hog was being butchered and that she was going to be too. She had commented to her folks several times that Gloria seemed to be friends with the hog and it was the strangest thing she had ever seen.

Gloria continued to sit on the couch and insisted that she was not going anywhere with her father. Shortly afterward, Bud returned from the slaughterhouse and Sylvia was not surprised to see Gloria retreat to the closet once again. Sylvia asked Bud, "Do you have any idea why Gloria believes that

she is supposed to be slaughtered with that hog you killed today?"

Bud shrugged and only replied, "Maybe it is because they are such good friends."

Bud and Sylvia began the process of packing, freezing, and cooking the pork that Bud had returned from the butcher's with. After a while, Sylvia called the rest of the kids, George, Dick, and Susan, into the kitchen for dinner. Bud said he would get Gloria, and Sylvia said it would probably be best to leave her until bedtime.

Bud soon decided that was not going to happen; he grabbed some fried pork skins and went over to the closet door. Bud opened the door and grabbed Gloria by the arm. "Look," he said, "I have some of your friend for you." Gloria began screaming and crying, and her father whispered in her ear, "Next week we will be frying you up and serving you at your precious Grandma's house." As her mother came around the corner, Gloria was screaming even louder and her father put his hand over her mouth and told Sylvia that Gloria wasn't going to be eating pork ever again.

{ 13 }

Helping Hurts

One of the neighbors that lived down the road, wasnear the Hebron Cemetery. Riding in the car one day, Gloria spotted a little girl playing outside. She was fascinated and began to look for the girl each time her mother drove by.

One day, she saw the girl playing outside as they were going by, and she decided to take matters into her own hands. Gloria's father had told her that those people were not the kind of people they wanted as friends. She planned to go find out if that was true or not. That day, she took a walk by herself to the little girl's house. When she got there, the girl was still outside playing, and she asked her if she could stay and play with her. The girl happily agreed and they began to talk as she brought out some toys to play with. She had the neatest toys—small plastic food, games, and all types of things. Gloria had never seen toys so nice.

Gloria would walk down to the girl's house whenever she could. She has been lonely during the day since Susie started school, and it was fun to have someone her age to play with. One day, George saw Gloria walking back from the other girl's house from the school bus as it passed her. After she got

home, Georgie asked Gloria about where she had been and why she was walking along the road. Gloria told him what house she had been going to and that there was a little girl there to play with. Georgie just smiled at her and warned Gloria not to walk so close to the road; it was dangerous.

One day, Georgie showed up at Gloria's friend's house to get her. He said, "Dad is really mad that you took off; Mom has dinner ready." Gloria told him that she would walk back right away, but Georgie told her to get on the front of his bicycle and he would give her a ride back.

Gloria was so excited; Georgie had rarely given her a ride on his bike. Georgie told her, "Watch out for your feet, and keep them pointed away from the spokes." Gloria got on the front of the bike and Georgie began to peddle back to their home. It was not far to their place, and soon, they made the turn up the curved drive to the back of the house.

Suddenly, Gloria felt her foot hit the spokes and go between them. Before she could even cry out, they were both on the ground, with Gloria's foot hurting bad. She cried and Georgie comforted her; leaving the bike where it fell, he carried Gloria the rest of the way to the house and up the back steps. George was limping a bit himself. When he came in the door carrying Gloria in his arms, their mom immediately took Gloria and laid her on the table to see how badly she was injured. George explained what had happened and Mom began to examine her foot. "It looks like she has a sprain," she said.

Their father walked into the room, slapped George across the face, and then began to beat him with his fists. He told

him that he was "stupid and should have known better that to put Gloria on the front of the bike." Mom got in the middle of the ruckus, and she was hit once for her trouble.

After she got things settled down, she put ice on Gloria's ankle and Gloria began to cry, trying to hold back her tears. "I am sorry," she said, "does the ice hurt?" Gloria began to cry harder; her mother asked her what was wrong.

Gloria began to wail through her tears, "I am sorry George, I am so sorry." Gloria felt if she had not gone to her friend's house to play, if only George had not had to come get her, their father would not have beaten him and hit her mommy. Even though George tried to tell her it was all right, she knew it was not; she could tell George was angry. Gloria also knew that if she did not quiet down, there would be trouble next time Mom went to work.

Gloria did not want to be the cause of George being hurt, or worse, the next time their father decided it was time for another lesson. It was as hard to watch those lessons as it was to be the one(s) chosen to participate. She did not even want to imagine how hard it would be to be the cause of George getting hurt like that. Gloria was afraid that one of these days, he was going to make George and her touch each other in the bad way. He had never done that before, but he had let Dick touch her and it was bad. The more Gloria had cried, the more they seemed to like it. It was hard for her to understand why they liked it when she cried, but only when they wanted her to; otherwise they kept telling her to shut up.

Bud could see that Georgie and Gloria had a good relation-ship despite their age difference. George warned Gloria that at some point, their father might try to make them do something. If that happened, George planned to leave. He said he could not take her with him, but he would send help. He thought that maybe Aunt Pete would be helpful when it came to their dad. Gloria thought that Aunt Pete did not care one way or the oth-er; she felt nothing from her. She was different from the other aunts. The aunts and uncles on the Crider side were close to Gloria and her siblings and any time she spent with them, she felt loved and cared for.

As a child, Gloria was unable to understand why her father and his sister hated them, or at the very least seemed to have no feelings at all for the kids. Grandma Peterson was a sweet and kind woman; nothing like her children.

{ 14 }

Kindergarten for Gloria

In September of 1960, when Gloria was just five years old, her mother came to her one day and told her to get dressed and be on her best behavior. She told her that she was going to kindergarten.

Gloria was so excited; she had been very lonely the past year after her big sister Susie started school. She would show Gloria all of the papers she brought home from school. They were full of numbers, shapes, and colors. Gloria was thrilled with what Susie was learning; Gloria often helped her correct the errors on her papers.

Sylvia was pregnant; she would give birth in the next several weeks, and she was hoping to find an alternative to sending Gloria to stay with her brother Blackie. Bud had refused to care for her.

Bud was refusing to take care of Gloria every day, all day, as he put it. She was too much of a baby for him, he said. This presented a problem because, if all went well, Sylvia would be in the hospital for at least a week. If things did not go well, it could be longer.

Sylvia knew that kindergarten had already begun this week and thought that maybe she could get Gloria enrolled. Sylvia knew that she was very smart, like her brother George, and maybe they would make an exception. Besides, Gloria was getting on her last nerve.

Gloria was a challenge when her father was not at home. She played hard and got herself into trouble constantly. She was also very inquisitive, asking a million questions a day. Sylvia thought it was no wonder that her brothers, sister, and all of her cousins had started calling her Magpie. She could challenge anyone's patience with all those questions.

Strangely, Gloria was a completely different child when her father was at home. In fact, most of the kids were very quiet when Bud walked through the door.

Sylvia loaded Gloria into the car and headed the few miles up Main Street to where the elementary and high school campuses where. Sylvia knew where to go since Susan had begun kindergarten last year. Gloria, two years younger than Susan, was ready for school. She hoped that she could convince the kindergarten teachers.

As Sylvia entered the classroom, she asked the teacher if she could speak to her outside. She told the teacher that she would like to enroll Gloria in kindergarten this year. The teacher asked what Gloria's age and birthday were. When Sylvia replied that Gloria had just turned five at the end of July, the teacher began to shake her head. Sylvia told the teacher that Gloria was a bit young but was extremely smart and more than capable of attending kindergarten. She pointed out to the

teacher that Gloria often had corrected her sister, Susan's work from kindergarten last year. She also told her that Gloria's brother was George Peterson, now a seventh grader, well known for his academic achievements.

The teacher acknowledged that George was very, very smart. She told Sylvia that even if Gloria was as smart as her brother, she was too young to be ready to attend school at five years old, especially given the fact that Gloria had just turned five two months previous. At that point, the teacher went over to the other kindergarten class and got the other kindergarten teacher to join the group in the hallway. She told the other teacher what Sylvia had already told her, and the other teacher agreed that Gloria was too young to be ready for school.

Sylvia, sensing she was losing, began to beg the teachers. She said, "Please, please let her go to school. I have no idea what I am going to do with her. She is so smart that she drives everyone crazy and even I have lost patience with her. Now I have another little one coming soon, and I need to make sure that she is busy so I can take care of the new baby."

Gloria stood by, stunned. *What*, she thought, *you cannot just decide to go to school and they let you?* She did not understand why the kindergarten teachers did not want her but understood that her mother was terribly upset by the refusal.

Gloria grabbed her mom's hand and whispered to her, "It's okay, Mommy, I will be good. Maybe I can go to school next year. This year I will be a really good girl and help you with the baby."

Sylvia turned to her daughter and knelt down to talk to her. "This means you will have to stay with Uncle Blackie and Aunt Pete. Will you be good and do that?"

Gloria's eyes got round in fear, but she told her mom, "I will go and be very good, just please don't leave me there very long." Sylvia hugged her little girl and they turned around and walked out of the school.

One of the two teachers said, as they were leaving, "Have you ever seen such a composed five-year-old? She understood everything that was going on and made her mother feel better when we said no."

Gloria heard that exchange and thought to herself, *They have no idea what happens when my father gets upset.* As much as Gloria disliked the idea of staying with her Aunt Pete, she hoped it would be okay, and it was far better than staying with her father.

Gloria, hurt by the things her mother told the teachers, felt unwanted and abandoned. Gloria decided it was not a good thing to let people know how smart she was. She decided no more questions, just keep quiet. It was probably safer.

{ 15 }

Butter You Up

Gloria thought it was unfair she should have to stay at Uncle Blackie and Aunt Marge's house while her mother was in the hospital. She knew that Mom was having a baby, and she was angry because her brothers and sister had been allowed to stay at home.

Gloria loved her Uncle Blackie, even though he scared her every July 4th, showing all the kids his hand that was missing most of his fingers. Along with the vision of those gruesome fingers, her uncle would tell all of the children about the grave dangers of fireworks. Her Aunt Marge was another story. Gloria was sure that her aunt did not like her at all. Her every look and word was filled with hate and anger, although Gloria was never quite sure why or what she had done to make her aunt angry. Everyone else Gloria knew called her aunt Pete, But Gloria would not call her that. Gloria never wanted people to call her Pete, not ever.

Out of all of her aunts and uncles, these two were different. Uncle Blackie was her mother's brother and Aunt Marge was her father's sister. Gloria had come to believe that her Aunt Marge hated her because her own father had told her to. She

avoided this aunt; all of her other aunts were from her mother's family and seemed much nicer, even showing her love. The cousins from this family were often referred to as her "double cousins" because they had the same bloodlines.

Every Sunday, all of the family gathered at Gloria's grandparents' house, on her mother's side. Her grandparents had a very large farmhouse that sat on fifty-five acres of fields and woods. With all of the cousins, aunts, and uncles, the Sunday gathering would often swell to more than forty people. Everyone pitched in preparing the dinner, and even the men would go into the woods on the farm and hunt rabbit and squirrel for dinner. Once the work was done, everyone would sit down and eat, sharing their week and talking about family matters. It was a place where Gloria felt safe. She never had to worry about bad things happening on those Sundays.

It was September of 1960, and the family gatherings were put on hold as school started and cooler weather began to take hold of the area in Culver, Indiana, where most of her mother's family lived. Gloria was too young for school, and so, when her mother went into labor, it was decided that Gloria would go to stay with her Aunt Marge and Uncle Blackie for a week. Her mother should be home by that time, and Gloria would have a new sister or brother when she came home.

Uncle Blackie's and Aunt Marge's home was a big, fancy house situated along Culver Road in Knox, Indiana. It was just a few miles east of Highway 35, the highway that ran north through town. It was also close to the Crider's Auto Body Shop owned by Blackie and his brother Rollie Crider.

The home was a single-level house with beautiful land-scaping and walkways, better than any others Gloria had ever seen. Aunt Marge had a big aquarium between the living and dining rooms, and Gloria was fascinated by it. There was a large back yard as well, with a swing set. Gloria avoided the swing set when she could because there were wasps in the poles to the swing set and she always wound up with a painful sting or two.

Uncle Blackie and Aunt Marge had three children of their own, Shirley, Ronnie, and Pat. Shirley was seven, the same age as Gloria's sister, Susie. Ronnie and Pat were older, twelve and thirteen, the same ages as Gloria's own brothers.

During the entire week, Gloria was sad and missed her mother and sister. Her Uncle Blackie would tease her and try to cheer her up, as would her two boy cousins. Shirley and her mother did little to make Gloria feel welcome. Shirley was annoyed that Gloria was there because she felt that Gloria was getting the attention that she would normally get from her mom and dad.

Her aunt did not work outside of the home; there was no need because Uncle Blackie and Uncle Rollie (another of her mother's brothers) owned the largest auto body shop in Knox. They had a very nice home and Aunt Marge kept it that way.

Aunt Marge seemed to value her nice things more highly than anyone or anything else. She would fuss and carry on if one of the children touched anything they should not. It seemed to Gloria that she was always walking on the wrong

floor, looking at the wrong thing, and generally just pissing her aunt off.

The week she stayed with them started off with Gloria just playing inside and outside to keep herself busy and to stay out of her aunt's way. As the week wore on, Gloria began to find it necessary to avoid her aunt. It seemed that her aunt was always angry with Gloria. It was frightening for the young girl and reminded her of her father. It was a feeling that made Gloria sick in the pit of her stomach.

The days passed slowly, and Gloria looked forward to the evenings when everyone else came home and she would be able to talk to someone who would not scream at her whenever she spoke. It made Gloria want to cry when her aunt screamed at her, but she knew better than to cry; her father would beat her if he heard.

Marge had dreaded having Gloria stay with her for a week. Her husband had volunteered, and her brother had jumped at the offer. Marge had never been able to stand her brother's youngest daughter. Marge felt the child was strangely quiet and kept everything to herself. Marge had tried slapping her once or twice to get her to obey, and the girl had just looked at her silently. She neither reacted nor obeyed. By the end of the fourth day Gloria had been with her, Marge was ready to burst with anger.

What Marge was unaware of was that Gloria was too afraid to respond, believing that her Aunt Marge was just like her father, and she could never trust what he told her. As her brother often said, "You are damned if you do and damned if

you don't" with him. Gloria was too young at five to understand the subtle subtext of what adults said, so she would just
stand there frozen in terror, believing that she was just as apt
to be beaten as not. There never seemed to be a right answer.

By the fifth night that Gloria was at their home, Marge was
just biding her time until the girl left in two days. Everything
had gone well with birth and Sylvia was leaving the hospital
soon. During the days when no one else was around, Marge
would yell and scream at Gloria for no reason whatsoever.
However, at night, once Blackie came home, Marge had to
hold herself back because Blackie would not allow her to hit
the child. No more than he allowed her to hit their own children in his presence.

That night, Marge made a wonderful dinner of pork chops,
corn, and mashed potatoes. Her mashed potatoes were so
smooth and had real butter in them. She was proud that she
was an excellent cook. Everyone was hungry, it was quiet during dinner, and no one talked much except to tell Marge how
good the food was. After the meal was over, everyone went
into the living room except Marge and Shirley who stayed
behind to clean up the dishes and put things away. Gloria also
stayed behind and offered to help, as she often did at home.
Marge, yelled at her to get out of the kitchen; she told her that
she didn't want her to help, saying that she was too fucking
stupid to help and would break something.

Gloria left the kitchen quickly before Marge could hit her
and went into the living room. As she walked to living room,

she began to cry softly. She had really wanted to help, hoping that maybe her aunt would be pleased with her.

When Blackie heard the yelling, he got up from the couch and met Gloria at the door. He placed his hand on her shoulder and told her not to worry, she did not need to help and that her aunt did not mean what she said. Blackie was glad that Gloria was leaving soon; he was a bit worried that Marge might hurt Gloria if she did not go home soon. He regretted having offered to take care of Gloria while his sister was in the hospital. She was such a small and shy girl, Blackie often wondered if Bud, his brother in law, beat her. He knew that he had put a stop to Marge's fits of temper in which she would literally whip their boys with a belt.

He took Gloria into the living room where he and his sons, Ronnie and Pat, were relaxing and talking about their day. As Blackie, Gloria, and the boys began talking, they all began to tease Gloria, hoping to lift her spirits. Gloria was a restrained child and was very shy at times. She was used to her uncle teasing her and her two cousins as well. They began to tease her about her dinner because she had not eaten very much. Ronnie began to ask her if she liked the rolls Aunt Marge had made. He asked her if she wanted to sit on his lap and she climbed up without any reservations. None of the uncles or cousins on her mother's side had ever given her reason to worry.

Settled on Ronnie's lap, they begin to trade banter about the delicious rolls that were served at dinner. Ronnie asked Gloria if she had put butter on her roll; he told her they were

so much better when they were all buttered up. The two of them laughed and Ronnie said, "A lot of things are better when they are buttered up." Still laughing, Gloria turned to Ronnie and said, "I will get a knife and butter you up so you will be good too."

At that moment, Marge burst through the door and started screaming at Gloria. "How dare you talk like that?" Marge yelled. She grabbed Gloria by the arm and began to hit her on her back and shoulders, screaming names at her as she kept hitting. Gloria was in shock and did not understand why her aunt was calling her names like "slut," "bitch," and "whore."

At that point, Uncle Blackie grabbed Marge by the arm and took Gloria from her, telling her to "get her hands off the child." They began to argue and Gloria was taken immediately to the bedroom that she was sharing with her cousin Shirley for the week. Pat helped her get ready and into bed. The last thing Gloria heard as she lay in the bed was her Uncle Blackie telling her aunt that she would do as he said or that would be the end of something. Gloria couldn't quite hear what that something was.

The next day began quietly enough; everyone was busy getting ready to go to work and school, but no one was talking much. Everyone was very subdued. Gloria was still unsure what had happened but was glad she only had one more day before she would see her mommy.

Later that morning after everyone else had gone; Gloria was alone in the house with her aunt. She was playing quietly on the floor in the living room and trying to behave the best

that she could. Gloria could feel the anger coming from her aunt in waves. She could hear her Aunt Marge muttering under her breath and whatever she was doing would get faster and louder the angrier she became.

At last, Aunt Marge got out the vacuum cleaner and began to vacuum the carpets. Gloria breathed a sigh of relief because as long as her aunt was vacuuming, Gloria could not hear her anger. As her aunt grew closer to where Gloria sat and played, Gloria began to pick up the toys she was playing with and move out of the way so that her aunt could vacuum. Without warning, Gloria felt something strike her hard across her back. She cried out as her aunt unleashed all of her fury on the child.

As Gloria cowered and tried to get away from her aunt, she felt the flexible hose from her aunt's vacuum cleaner hitting her across her back, on her legs and butt. She thought that it was the vacuum hose but couldn't quite see it. Gloria ended up cowering in a corner while her aunt vented all of her pent up anger on her. She spat a constant stream of vicious words at the child as Gloria hunched over and tried to protect her head and arms from the attack. "You little slut bitch cunt," her aunt said repeatedly at Gloria. Each time she brought the hose down on Gloria's backside, she would say it again.

Finally, she slowed her attack and told Gloria, "How dare you talk to my son about buttering him up; he is just a child, and you are an evil, evil whore." Gloria was not sure what "butter you up" meant that was nasty, but Gloria decided that it was not good. In fact, Gloria was very confused but decided

not to use those words ever again. Gloria tried to tell her aunt that she was sorry, but her aunt would just hit her again and say, "Shut up, you slut!"

That night, Gloria asked to go to bed right after dinner. She was afraid that she might say the wrong thing again, and she still hurt from the beating earlier that day. She hurt too badly to sleep and was afraid that her aunt would attack her while she slept. She wished her mommy would hurry and come get her.

The next morning, Sylvia arrived with the new baby, Sharon, to pick Gloria up and take her home. Sylvia's brother, Blackie had called her and told her about Marge picking on Gloria. As Sylvia looked at her daughter, she noticed that Gloria had a few bruises on her legs. As she lifted Gloria's shirt, she found more bruises on her back and shoulders. Gloria heard the sharp intake of breath her mother made when she lifted the shirt. Sylvia knew that Gloria had been beaten; she asked her what had happened. As Gloria started to tell her, Marge walked into the living room and told Sylvia that Gloria had fallen off the swing set. When Sylvia asked Gloria what happened, Gloria responded with stony silence.

Sylvia stood up and told Marge to go into the kitchen with her. Gloria could hear them yelling but was too engrossed in the tiny baby her mother had brought home to pay attention. Sylvia came out of the kitchen telling Marge over her shoulder, "Blackie warned me about your temper, but I never thought you would hurt a child. Never touch one of my kids again or you can be sure I will make you pay."

Marge countered with, "Take care of your own damn kids then."

Sylvia ended the confrontation as she told her that she never needed to worry about taking care of any of the kids again, not hers or any of the other nephews and nieces. She said, as she left, "I will make sure the entire family knows you are not fit to care for children. Blackie told me that he had your temper under control, but you apparently have him fooled."

{ 16 }

Another One Too Many

Bud was having a difficult time. He was impatient and wanted to get on with it. He had stopped getting a good charge out of thinking about the last child born to Sylvia. He was bored and looking for someone to supply him with entertainment.

He had stepped up the intensity of the "training" he was performing on the kids. The oldest girl, Susan, was particularly becoming adept at accepting whatever was done to her. Sometimes he would just sit and watch as his youngest boy, Dick, would molest the girl. Other times, his impatience would get the best of him. He would get up and slug Dick in the face and then start slapping the two girls and subjecting them to other enticing activities.

Once, he bound both of the girls' hands and feet; then he began slapping their feet with spatulas from Sylvia's kitchen. Other times, he would force them to kneel and then have them lick his penis. Sometimes he would just force them to watch as he butt-fucked one or the other of the boys, telling them that they needed to learn what butt fucking was and be ready to have him shove his cock up their butts.

As intense as the pain and shame of these activities were for the girls and the boys, none of it measured up to the intense excitement he felt that June day in the Crider woods. He remembered the power he felt and the release as he killed and then disposed of the infant.

Now, there was a new baby in the house and Bud just couldn't stop thinking about the possibilities. He often watched the baby sleeping while Sylvia was at work. He would masturbate while he formulated a plan to "dispose" of this baby as well. However, it was late November and soon the Christmas season would begin. He didn't want to begin his plan until after Christmas, but he was wary of waiting too long. He really didn't feel badly about what he was planning. He had warned Sylvia that she should not get pregnant again, so this was her fault, not his.

In order for his plan for this girl to work, he needed a different excuse than the last time. His plan necessitated the kid being sick, and that would mean he needed to wait until that happened. Still, that was taking some time and Bud knew that the older this one got, the more risk that he might be caught.

Eventually, after New Year's Day, this one got sick with a bad cold. Bud had been opening the window next to the crib and leaving it open until just before Sylvia got home from work in the wee hours of the morning. He would close the bedroom door so the other kids did not see.

Sylvia had taken Sharon to the doctor that day to see just how bad her cold was. She had taken great care to keep her warm and away from other sick children. However, she had

caught a cold anyway. Now she took her home and set up a tent over the crib and took out the vaporizer and turned it on so that Sharon could breathe better.

Bud was thrilled when he realized that his plan was in action. He could hardly wait to get started, and better yet, Sylvia herself had supplied the weapon.

That night, after all of the kids were asleep and before Sylvia came home, Bud prepared the next step in his plan. He went into the kitchen and put water in the pan that Sylvia used to heat bottles for the baby. He placed the pan on the stove and turned up the heat. He watched the water heat up, his senses heightened in anticipation. He could feel the length of his cock heating up as the water started to boil. He had a bottle of formula in his hand just in case someone came in and asked him what he was doing.

When the water was just to boiling, he placed the formula back in the refrigerator; he was not going to need it for this. He had considered what direction to take at this point and wondered if he should change his mind. He had planned to throw the boiling hot water on the child's stomach, hoping that the burn would be bad enough to kill her. However, as he walked to the bedroom, he had a better idea. He reasoned that if the water were on her stomach, it would not make as much sense as if he poured it on her face. By pouring it on her face, it would appear to be a malfunction of the vaporizer. In addition, it had the potential for more serious damage and he wanted the infant dead.

Bud had been entertaining himself with the other four kids and was finding that the more intense the pain, the more intense his orgasm was. He did not enjoy pain himself but enjoyed the sight and sound of pain from others very much.

As soon as he walked back into the bedroom, he tossed the water on the baby's face and immediately returned to the kitchen and placed the pan back on the stove.

The infant immediately began to scream and squirm with intense pain. Her lower face was red and blistered. One spot was even sloughing off, leaving a bright red spot of raw skin that covered one-half of her lower face.

George, wakened by the screaming, went into his parent's room and crossed to the crib. He saw what looked like a bad burn on his little sister's face and went into the kitchen to call an ambulance. When he got there, he found his father, Bud, standing against the sink. "What is all of the screaming about?" asked Bud. George told him about Sharon's burn. Bud shrugged his shoulders and asked him, "What are you waiting for, call an ambulance."

George picked up the telephone and called the number for the ambulance that his mother had posted there. Then, George dialed the number for his mother's job. Getting no answer, George figured that his mother was already on the way home.

As Sylvia got closer to home, she could see the red and blue flashing lights of emergency vehicles. She was tired and it was very dark, so she was unable to see where the trouble was until she got much closer. Her stomach leapt into her throat and fell as a sense of dread sunk in. "Please, not my

house. Not my house." Sylvia cried. However, as she got closer, she could see it was her house. She pulled up in front of the house so that she didn't block in the ambulance that she was now sure was in her driveway. As Sylvia ran from the car, an ambulance attendant came out of the house carrying a very small bundle in his arms. She cried, "Oh no, what is wrong, is she okay?"

The ambulance attendant replied, "It is a very bad burn, Ma'am, she needs to go to the hospital." He asked Sylvia if she would like to ride along with them and she agreed and jumped up into the back of the ambulance.

When they got Sharon strapped in and began to back out and move, Sylvia asked if he knew what happened. The attendant told her that her husband said the vaporizer exploded on the girl's face. Then the attendant added, "I have seen a lot of vaporizer burns, Mrs. Peterson, and this does not look like one. Also, there was too much water on the crib for it to be the vaporizer, unless someone picked it up and threw it on her." Sylvia was shocked into silence; she never thought that anyone would go as far as to burn the baby; she just could not absorb it. The attendant added, "I cannot prove that anything wrong was done, Ma'am, it is just a feeling."

Just at that point, the ambulance arrived at the hospital and Sharon was rushed into the emergency room. Her burns were dressed and she was held under observation for a few days. They watched her for infection and waited for her cold to clear up. After she was getting better and her burns were healing well, she was sent home. Her doctor told her mother that

she should heal well without scarring because she was so young.

Sylvia was beginning to think that this was one too many coincidences. She remembered her last daughter cold and blue in her crib. She also recalled not being able to find any trace of her infant daughter after Bud left the house with her that day. She was worried about the kids but felt trapped and powerless to do anything. She could not prove anything, and Bud was good at making her look like she was to blame for things that went wrong. No one believed that Bud could do any wrong. She planned to keep a sharp eye on him, somehow.

{ 17 }

Practice Makes Imperfect

Bud was a skilled worker. After his time in the military during World War II, he often worked as a crane operator or drafter. By 1952, however, he was working only as a general laborer. Bud usually worked as a construction worker, so his work relied upon good weather. It also relied on two other things—a good economy as well as Bud himself to go to the union hall to register for work.

Having been born into a hard-working union home, Bud was familiar with the requirements of raising a family and having a home. Now, it seemed that Bud was tired of working to provide for his family. He stopped going to the union hall to check for work. The few contractors he had worked for regularly tired of his tardiness and frequent absence on the job. Several contractors had called the union hall in Valparaiso and demanded that Bud not be assigned to any of their jobs. Bud had gone a few times to the union hall in Hammond, Gary and even Plymouth, but it seemed that word had spread.

Dammit! Bud thought as he pulled away from the union hall. Bud did not understand why the union was blacklisting

him. What did people expect? It was a union job; you took the jobs you wanted and let the rest of them do without you. Bud was angry at the rejection; he had not done anything to deserve this kind of treatment. *Sure, he was late a few times,* he thought, *but that was Sylvia's fault.* If she had not left him weighed down with all those kids, he would not have been late so many times. He certainly would not have to drink so much that he missed work either.

The truth was that Bud had gone to work drunk and mean so many times, most of the supervisors had become afraid to have him working on their jobs. Bud had several fights and arguments with both his co-workers and bosses. Bud, at six foot-four inches tall, was a powerful man. Once the word got around about the way he acted on the job, it was only a matter of time before he would have to look for a new line of work.

Bud's father had passed away in 1954, leaving Bud without any kind of anchor. Bud had hated his father, hated how brutally he treated him. Nonetheless, his father was the only example Bud had to follow. Bud was also relieved when his father passed away. Bud's father, George Senior, was Bud's worst critic and even after he was an adult, his father's criticisms had still cut like a knife.

Now, his mother, Grace, came to stay with his family on alternating weekends. The other weekend was spent at his sister's house with her three kids and his brother-in-law. Bud was not happy to have her in his home that often, but Sylvia got along well with his mother. Sylvia had insisted that Grace stay for both her and the kids' sake. The problem, as Bud saw

it, was that his ability to have practice sessions with the kids would be limited by her presence. On the other hand, she had a way with the kids that he did not recall from his own childhood. Bud wondered why his own mother loved his children more than she had ever loved him or his siblings. He believed that his mother loved his kids simply because they were from some other father than his own. Looking back, Bud did not blame her. It never occurred to him that she might love the kids because they were his children.

It was strange to Bud how accepting Sylvia and her family were of his family members and all of the in-laws, no matter how bad the family they came from was. Bud and his father certainly were never that accepting of anyone.

Bill and Nona Crider had even purchased a cemetery plot with enough spaces for themselves, each of their children, and their children's spouses. That said a lot about Bill and Nona as parents and parents-in-law. They also allowed their children to make their own mistakes and never criticized them. The whole family was the same, never airing the family laundry in public; they never even bad-mouthed another family member among themselves.

In the past few years, Bud had been working less and less. He would take a job when one fell down in front of him and he felt that he could not avoid it. Other times he would cut wood from his in-laws' woods and sell it on the side so that he would have money for booze. It was not much, but it kept Sylvia from knowing how much he was spending on alcohol or losing at gambling.

With no work during the day, Bud would take off and go into Knox; he spent his days gambling or drinking at the VFW or the American Legion Hall. The gambling had to be on the sly since it was not a legitimate activity. When it started getting late, he would head home to eat dinner. He tried to delay going home until he knew for sure that Sylvia had left for work.

As Bud considered his situation, he decided that not working would leave him more time to devise some new special practice sessions with the kids.

His mother, especially attached to Susan and Gloria, would take the girls shopping or to the movies and make things for them. The smallest items seemed to make the girls happy. Grace once made each girl a hand-tatted handkerchief, and both girls slept with their handkerchiefs. It was plain to Bud that the girls placed a great value on the gifts that his mother had given them.

It was a plan for one of his practice sessions to take those "precious" gifts away from the girls. Who were they, anyway? Bud felt that his kids should not receive more love and attention from his mother than he or his siblings ever did. Once he had taken the gifts from them, the girls would understand that he had more power than anyone else did to control their lives.

Creating control over the kids was foremost; in order to make sure that they did not tell anyone what he was doing, he used fear to control the kids. He understood what worked with one might not work with another, so he used different tactics with the boys than the girls.

With the girls, he knew that the chicken slaughter terrified them both. Watching Vern first lay a chicken on the chopping block, chopping the head off the bird at the neck, and then releasing the chicken's body to writhe and flop all over the yard was very scary to any young child. In order to impress on them the important of keeping their mouths shut, he told them that if they told anyone, he would make them watch as he cut off their mother's head and let her flop, screaming all over the place. He was sure this made an impression because both of the girls' eyes were as big as saucers.

With the boys, ages eleven and twelve, he just promised to give their mom a beating, worse than any they had ever seen. Then as soon as he was through, he would beat them until they bled, if they told.

So frequently, on nights when he had to be alone with the kids while their mother ran off to work, he would hold a practice session. It was unpredictable when these sessions would happen. However, after his father died in 1954 and until 1961, Bud worked on perfecting both his hold over the kids and his technique in exacting the most fear and pain from the sessions. The sessions kicked into high gear once the family moved from the home in Hammond to their new place in Hebron, Indiana.

Each practice session was different, largely based on Bud's immediate desire for power, control, sexual release, or just plain entertainment. He would decide who would be a participant in the session and who would be a spectator. This would be resolved by sensing who had the most fear as he set up the

equipment he planned to use. Over time, the spectators learned never to intervene in the session for the participants. If they did, they would soon find that Bud had plans for them too.

The kids agreed between them that no matter whether they were participant or spectator, they would do their best not to hurt each other. They really had no idea what Bud had in mind for them.

Bud planned another "session" with the kids; he wanted to perfect his technique on the water "shocking" he had tried on the girls. He had not really given it much forethought; it had been more of a moment of opportunity. He believed that water could carry a shock, delivered to each girl in the tubs he had filled with cold water. He had used 12-volt DC batteries. Reading more about electrical charges, Bud discovered that water only acted as a conduit for the charge. The water carried a charge that traveled through the girls' bodies but delivered no shock. He had noticed lines on the girls' bodies as they were removed from the tubs. The lines were where the water had touched their bodies and left a kind of a general swelling. He also realized that the semi-conscious state the girls had seemed to be in was probably only mild hypothermia.

This time, Bud wanted a much more painful and fearful effect. He could get off on that. He had been very disappointed the last time. His reading had given him some better ideas. He gathered a few of the newer 9-volt batteries, some sewing pins, and made up a half dozen alligator clamps. Ready to get started, he called the kids into the laundry room and had them

stand in a line behind him. With his back to the kids, Bud assembled the 9-volt battery "shockers" and laid them out on the laundry sink's drain-board. As he turned around, he told the boys to get a chair from the kitchen and place it in the laundry room next to the sink.

He thought to himself that he should have the designated "spectators" help in the "training" by causing the pain to their "participating" siblings. He was awed by his amazing intellect; it would give him something to "hold over" the spectators' heads should they decide to rebel. It would also give him an opportunity to create an assistant, someone like himself. Whichever kid appeared to enjoy the infliction of pain and fear might be trained to assist him as a position of power over the others.

Next, Bud had Susie sit in the chair and take off her clothes. He chose Susie because she was least likely to scream aloud as he experimented with his new toy. She also had the most sexual experience of the two girls.

Bud first took the alligator clip and, pulling on Susie's nipple, he placed the clamp on her breast. Susie screamed in surprise and Bud laughed and told the others, "This is how you don't want to attach this." He then hooked the alligator clamp to the battery and then wrapped the bare wires around one of the sewing pins. He then took the supplies he had and made another device. He then pulled a glove on his hand and walked back over to Susie. He took the girls breast again and started to insert the pin into her breast. As he got close to the skin, Susie shrank back, crying, and tried to move away from

him. He had Dick stand behind her and hold her still. He realized that he would have to remove the wire from the pins. After he removed the wires, he unclipped the alligator clamp from the battery. He inserted the pin into the skin of Susie's small breast, and Dick held his hand over her mouth as their father completed his task. Ignoring the blood dripping down Susie's nipple, Bud wrapped the wire on the pin once again up next to the pinhead so it would not slip off.

Bud was already happier with this method than the last based on the amount of pain and fear he felt in the room. Next, he picked up the battery and touched the clamp to the battery terminals. It was a small discharge, but enough to make Susie jump. Bud told Dick to take his hand off Susie's mouth and "Let her scream. I want to hear it all." Bud continued to touch the clamp to the battery terminals, extracting a small cry of pain from Susie each time.

Dick was fascinated and watched closely. Bud told Susie to put her legs on each side of the chair and told Dick to hold her down. Bud then took another wire, and instead of inserting a pin, taped the bare ends to her leg. When he touched the battery to the clamp, he got the same result.

Bud decided that two would be better, and he told George to get another chair and place it next to Susie. As George walked into the room, he argued with Bud that Gloria was too small for him to stick pins in. Bud told him to "Shut up and put the chair where I told you, or you will be next." Bud moved the wire from Susie's leg and placed it between her legs to see what happened. The response was much more

other nipple quickly. He wound the wire around the ends of the pins. As an afterthought, Bud took two of the clamps in his hand. He took his thumb and tweaked Gloria's nipples to gauge the pain that would result. He was pleased with the pain that action produced, and he told Dick to hold her down. Dick put his hands on Gloria's shoulders and then reached forward and tweaked Gloria's nipples the way he had seen his father do.

Bud watched as Dick thrummed Gloria's nipples with one hand and held her to the chair with the other. He could see from Dick's breathing and the way his eyes dilated, Dick was becoming quite excited. He stopped the boy and told him that he could have more fun next time. Bud then took a battery and made contact with the clamp. He could see that the effect of the shock was less than the pain created by the pins and clamps.

Bud decided that the shocking was not as effective as he would like. He would need to study more for the next time. Disappointed, he left the room, warning the kids once again what would happen if anyone found out about their training.

{ 18 }

More Practice

Gloria found that if she tuned out during these "torture sessions" her father enjoyed so much, she was able to deal with the anxiety, fear, and shame she experienced with each session. Logically, she found this much easier to do when she was a spectator, but less so when she was the recipient of her father's attention.

Gloria realized that she could not maintain control over her emotions easily while she was in great pain and was afraid of dying. She was able to block some of the horror and fear when forced to watch the activities. She turned her thoughts internally, and while she could not block all of the horrible things that were going on, she could control her anxiety. Gloria learned to stuff her feelings deep inside and was able to block the memories to some extent.

The sessions continued, unrelenting. Bud was developing some techniques he had read about in library books. Bud would take cord and tie up the kids' feet and hands behind them. He would loop the cord up around their necks, padding it where it lay in the front. If they struggled, they would begin to tighten the cord and lose oxygen, and the padding would

make sure no marks were left. Bud liked the results he got with this; he had practiced on himself when he masturbated and knew that it resulted in heightened senses. He had heard about the asphyxia technique from a friend. Bud determined that no matter what the emotion—fear, pain, or sexual arousal—the effect could be magnified by reducing the amount of oxygen to the brain. He had to be careful not to go too far. It would be impossible to explain a death of one of the kids that way.

When Bud tied up one of the kids, he would slap and punch them to get them to move and tighten the cords. He would also take his belt and whip them on the bottoms of their feet. Once he felt the kid was in a state of heightened senses, he would molest the child to see if the effect was the same as his.

Sometimes, Bud would simply have one or both of the girls lie face down on the floor. Next, he would lie on top of the girl using the full force of his weight to crush the girl against the floor and encourage one of the boys to get on top of the other girl. Using his weight to keep the girl immobile, Bud would start dry humping the girl, both of them fully clothed. Crushing with the added pressure of the movement was extremely painful to the girls. Gloria often told Susie that it hurt as if her bones were breaking, and she thought that it would hurt less if he just killed her and ended it. When her father did this to her, Gloria would just go inside herself and stop moving; it seemed easier that way. If she or her sister struggled during one of these sessions, it was far more painful.

Susie, however, would struggle uselessly and try to yell through the gag shoved into her mouth.

During one particularly brutal session, Bud announced to the group that he was going to kill one of the kids during the session. He had a knife, a shotgun set to one side, and he had the kids line up four chairs and sit down. He took cord and tied their arms behind their backs to the chair. He then took longer pieces of rope and tied all of their legs, going down the line from George the oldest to Gloria the youngest.

Once the kids were secured, he began to assign tasks; some were for all the kids and some were individual. First, he told all of the kids to lower their pants so that they were down around their feet. Realizing that he had tied their hands, he untied Gloria and forced her to undo and lower the pants of both of her brothers and her sister. As she went down the line, she struggled to accomplish her feat. Her brothers would look at her face and lift their rear so that she could pull their pants down. Seeing their tears, Gloria began to weep and apologize to each of them. When she got back to her chair, her father told her to pull her panties down and sit in the chair; at that point, he tied her hands and legs again.

He started with Gloria, took his knife and made a cut on her arm. It was not a deep cut, but it hurt and Bud wanted these kids to know who had all of the power. He stuck his hands between her legs and grabbed her hard. He told Gloria that she was a "no good cunt" and made her repeat it. He then told Gloria to tell him who had the power to end her life. Not

really understanding what he was asking Gloria replied, "God."

This angered Bud, so he slapped the girl across the face and grabbed her between her legs again and said, "This is what you are, just a dirty little cunt." Gloria cried and wished that he would stop what he was doing and move on to her sister. Immediately, Gloria felt guilty for that wish and got quiet.

Bud moved on to Susie and punched her in the stomach. He grabbed her between her legs and said, "You are a filthy cunt, and don't forget it." He asked Susie, "Who has the power to end your life?"

Susie replied, "You do."

As he slapped Susie's face, he finished with, "That is right and don't you forget it, you stupid cunt."

Moving on to Dick, Bud noticed that Dick had an erection. Bud looked at him and asked him, "You liked that, huh?" Dick nodded his head yes and flinched back just in case his father planned to punch him. The kids could never tell what would anger Bud. To that, Bud reached behind Dick and untied his hands. "Go ahead, take care of yourself," he said. As Dick began to rub himself, his father stood before him and laughed, "You are a sorry fuck, you know that? You have two completely bare cunts right here and you want to rub your cock." Dick just nodded and put his head down.

Bud moved on to George, and putting his knife to George's neck said, "I should probably kill you; you are too old to be much fun anyway. But, if I do that, then I will be stuck cleaning up."

Bud stood, picked up his shotgun and hollered, "Change of plans." He told Dick to get on the floor and to lie down near the floor drain. He untied his legs and jerked him up hard from the chair. "I am sorry, but you have to go," Bud said to Dick as he walked him over to lie on the floor. Dick lay on the floor, his hands behind his back.

Gloria was immediately in flight mode; she tried to stand up and run, forgetting she was tied to the chair. Bud raised the shotgun, aimed at her, and said, "Sit back down, unless you want me to shoot you too." Gloria sat down; there was no way to escape what was about to happen and no way not to watch. Gloria began to retreat into her head but she was so afraid that she was unable to. She looked around at her brothers and sisters and could feel their fear. They had not thought that Bud would kill somebody, but now it seemed that they may have been wrong.

Bud turned to Dick and told him to look at the wall. As he lay there, Bud aimed the shotgun at Dick's back and counted down from ten. As he got to three, Dick peed in his pants and Bud prodded him with the shotgun. Two, one, and as Bud pulled the trigger on the shotgun, there was a loud click. All four of the kids jumped at the sound of that click and then slowly realized that the shotgun had not fired. "Bang," Bud yelled and walked out of the room laughing. Over his shoulder, he shouted back to the kids, "Never forget I can pull the trigger on a loaded shotgun just as easily as one that is not loaded. Dick, get off your ass and untie the others."

Now that the kids were convinced that he would kill them, Bud planned to increase the pace by having training sessions several nights a week. Bud was sure that the work he had done so far had the girls ready for what he wanted to try next. If not, he would conduct thorough training sessions to make sure. Bud wanted to experiment with the kids sexually. Bud thought by training the kids to perform sex acts, he was getting the boys ready for life and the girls ready to be the worthless whores they were destined to be. Bud decided that if he got any inkling that the kids had any doubts about doing as he said, he could always have more sessions to increase their fear.

The way Bud planned the sex sessions, he could do it in any combination he liked. As he began his first session, he had the boys put their cocks in the girls' mouths. George was reluctant, so Bud gave him Gloria, figuring that she would not be any good anyhow. Besides, George had always been protective of that one for some reason. *Maybe he is already messing with her*, Bud thought. Then he dismissed the thought; no one was as smart as he was, but George was close.

Susie, forced to do this before, had experience; Gloria, however, did not have any idea what to do. Soon, Bud got bored watching this and told the kids to stop. Bud had Dick suck George's cock and watch as George looked at his brother with distaste. Bud was getting hard, and he pushed George aside and stuck his own cock into Dick's mouth. Once their father was busy, both girls decided that they could slip out of the room before things got worse. As they crept around the

corner, they heard their father say, "Get the fuck back in here." They both turned and walked back to the room.

Bud told the girls to take off their clothes and get on the floor. When the girls lay face down, Bud told them to roll over. Bud was getting more excited watching his son suck his cock but wanted this to last longer. He was feeling very powerful and liked that feeling. He had Dick stop sucking and stroking his cock. He told both of the boys to sit down next to one of their sisters. Dick immediately went over to Susie and sat next to her. George sat next to Gloria. Bud told the boys to take off their pants and rub their cocks until they were hard. "Now," he said, "you girls put your hand on that cock and see what a hard cock feels like. Boys, take your hand and rub the girl's pussy and see what that feels like." He told them to keep rubbing so he could think of what he wanted to do next. The girls were crying, and he figured there was no way for them to get off. He had really wanted to see them climax, so this was a bitter disappointment. He told the boys to masturbate and ejaculate on the girls.

Dick said, "No, I want her to finish sucking my cock." This distracted Bud, and he had Dick put his cock back into Susie's mouth. He was so engrossed in watching Dick that he forgot all about the other two kids. As Dick grabbed Susie's head and slammed into her, Bud was becoming more excited. He joined the two on the floor and began rubbing Susie between her legs. Susie, terrified, started to move away and Bud told her sit still. Bud tired of the girl and told Dick to change positions. "I want you to lick her," Bud told him, "while I

fuck your ass." Dick knew this was going to hurt and tried to ignore him while he finished with Susie. Bud told him, "Don't forget what I will do if you don't do what you are told." Dick switched positions and bared himself to his dad, who shoved his penis in so hard that Dick yelled. Bud slammed his fist into Dick's back and continued to pound away at his back while he raped him. Dick, in his fury and pain, put his face between Susie's legs and bit her. George and Gloria had watched, forgotten as the session unfolded before them, each with a feeling of dread that they would be next and guilt that they had received a reprieve. Gloria thought, angry for her sister, *If Dick ever puts his cock in my mouth, I am going to bite it!*

Once Bud was finished, he felt disappointed. Things had not gone as he planned. He thought that the boys would have enjoyed sex, no matter whom it was with, and that they should have thanked him for the chance he had just given them. He found that they were all about themselves and ungrateful for his efforts. The girls were still too young to know what was happening; they should have at least pretended to enjoy it. He intended to change that.

He would have to slow it down until they became more accustomed to the activity; he also decided that George was not going to be helpful, and he would have Dick help him with the girls. He would teach Dick how to control the girls and get what he wanted. He was beginning to feel good about his plan again and powerful.

First, he needed to take care of George.

The day after the first sex training, Bud waited until after dinner, and he asked George to come talk to him in the backyard. George was angry about the sex training but was afraid of his father. He decided that he was only going to do that again if he had to. He did not like what was going on but was too afraid of this father to tell anyone.

Bud and George walked out of the backyard and into the walnut grove. As they stopped, Bud reached out and punched George in the face. It did not hurt badly; George had built up a tolerance to the pain and terror over time. Bud told George that he was very disappointed in his performance the night before and wanted him to know it. He also told George that because he was such a waste of talent, he was only going to have Dick help him teach the girls about sex from then on. George was suspicious and told his father that what he was doing to his sisters was wrong. Bud punched him several times and called him a "pussy." Bud told him that while they were training from now on he could stay inside. Bud was planning to move the training out to the barn, he told him. He would have more room and equipment in the barn. George did not like the sound of that but did not question. He was glad to be out of the sessions. He knew that there was something seriously wrong with their father and did not know what to do about it.

{ 19 }

Bud Stops Working

Bud spent most of his time developing his techniques, so Bud stopped working altogether. He could not be bothered with mundane things like working. He was becoming addicted to the excitement and power he had over the kids. He still thought five kids were too many, but George was taking care of the infant for him. That left him more time with the other three.

Before he and George had struck this deal, there was an imbalance in the sessions. There were three males to only two females. This new combination of two on two seemed easier. He did not have to force George to participate in the sexual stuff, so there was one girl for him if he wanted.

Sylvia was complaining bitterly about the lack of financial support he provided. He just yelled back at her until she shut up and let it die. He did not care if she could not make the house payments. He did not care if the car needed tires, or if there was no gas for her to get to work. He just did not care about anything other than knowing when she was leaving for work so his work could resume.

Recently, one of the girls had been complaining that her pee-pee was itching. He decided he should stop experimenting by putting whatever he thought of inside the girls' cunts. He did not want to make one of them sick; that might result in being found out. He chuckled and thought to himself, *I don't care if they get sick; I just don't want to get caught.*

Sunday, Sylvia had shown him a letter from the bank about the mortgage. It was a Notice of Default. She told him that they had only thirty days to cure the default or foreclosure would begin. Sylvia began to cry; she wanted to know why he was not working and trying to help her keep their home. Bud just made a disgusted sound and left the house.

Later that week, Sylvia told Bud that she had spoken to the bank and they told her that she could sign a deed in lieu of foreclosure. That would give the family sixty days to find a house and move out of the property. She told Bud that she had agreed and the paperwork was in the process.

Bud was ballistic. "How dare you talk to the bank without my approval!" Bud continued to yell for about thirty minutes, throwing accusations at Sylvia and calling her names. He was upset and worried that he would have to do all of the moving. He told Sylvia to "get her ass back down to the bank and tell them she has changed her mind."

Sylvia waited for Bud to stop yelling and demanding. When he took a break to breathe, she asked him, "Do you have the money to pay the bank?" She said, "I would hate to lose this place and all of the work and money we put into it."

Bud turned to Sylvia and told her in a nasty tone, "Are you stupid or what? Do I look like I have money? I have not worked for almost a year and a half."

Sylvia sighed and said, "We are going to have to move by the end of next month. I have found a small place that we can afford."

Bud flew into a rage again. "I told you that you have no right to do these things behind my back."

Sylvia looked at him squarely and told him, "One of us had to take care of things."

During the next weeks, all of the Petersons' personal belongings were packed and then loaded on a trailer. Sylvia had found a small home that would hold all of them. She could make the rent if she worked a few more hours and would still be able to buy food. Sylvia spent every Sunday cleaning the new place in the sixty days before they had to vacate the home she had loved. *It was just a home*, she told herself, and she could make a new home anywhere she and her kids were.

The home Sylvia found was far worse than the one they had lived in. The home was small with a low and patched roof. It had three bedrooms, a combined living and kitchen area, and one bathroom. The rooms were small and cramped with the furniture they brought with them. There was also a cellar with a dirt floor.

Gloria was in first grade when they moved to the small house. She remembered riding the bus to the elementary school. She especially liked the days that her brother, George, was on the bus too. She felt special when George would take

her to the back of the bus where the older kids sat and let her ride to school on his lap. It was not until she was older that she realized he probably let her ride there to get the attention of some of the girls on the bus with them.

There was a house, just up the road from their new home, which was huge. The Petersons' new place was on a narrow country road, outside of town. Gloria knew the little girl her age who lived there and made friends with her. The two girls would play outside of the big house and sometimes indoors. The house was more beautiful inside than any house Gloria had ever seen. There were lots of room, and the girls could play games and talk for hours until Gloria had to go home around dinnertime. Gloria was allowed to play at the neighbor's house infrequently. Her father made her stay close to her own house in the event he made plans for them.

Bud stopped the training at the new house. He was irritated because he had to rethink his plans. With no barn, no laundry room, and no shed, Bud would have to figure out where he would be able to train the kids undiscovered.

However, it did not take Bud long to decide where to start his plan again. The house had a basement with a dirt floor and low ceiling. Sylvia had expressed her disgust and unease with the basement and never entered it.

Bud moved right in; he took all of his tools from the workshop and all of his training tools and set the boxes along one wall. For the first few weeks, Bud made cage traps to catch squirrels and rabbits. He justified the cost of this to Sylvia by

pointing out the woods at the back of the house and telling her that he would be catching game for dinners.

Bud was in no hurry to get started; he needed to find out how close the nearest neighbors were. He was on a much smaller parcel and wanted to make sure there were no nosy neighbors. He made sure that he would not be trespassing on anyone's land in the woods. Bud did not care if he was, he just did not welcome the unexpected intrusion that may come of it.

Bud had big plans for the new training sessions. The same old training was not delivering the charge it once did; he was restless and bored. Bud set and baited his traps around the woods, not too far from the house. He spent days at estate auctions and junk stores looking for implements to add to his collections. One day, he came upon eight steel spring-jawed traps. Bud bought the eight traps and added them to his collection in the basement.

Bud looked around the basement and began to implement his new plan for training. *To be truthful*, he thought, *these sessions are going to be more about pain and fear.* He was not able to persuade any of the kids, except Dick, that there was anything pleasurable about the other sessions. Bud was sure it was just that the girls were too young to feel sexual pleasure, not because his training was a failure. He decided that, to first convert the girls to help him achieve maximum impact, he would have to show them the limits of fear and pain he could inflict. In addition to that, Bud needed to reinforce his power over them.

Bud set the basement up for the next training session. He took two shovels and two small spades and propped them up against the wall of the basement. Next, Bud took some spare wood from outside and sat it up on either side of the opening into the basement. After he was done, Bud looked it over closely. He wanted to make sure that his "special guests" would be routed into the area of the basement he intended.

Last, Bud set up all eight steel spring-jawed traps, spacing them along the track he had set up. The traps would be difficult to avoid for his "special guests," and if they managed to avoid the traps, he would kill them with the shovels.

Bud went out into the woods and checked his cage traps. He found that only three traps had been triggered. Bud picked up the traps and carried them, one at a time, back to the basement entrance.

The kids had all arrived home from school, but Sylvia had not left for work yet. Fortunately, she was uninterested in what he had been doing. Bud went inside and washed up for dinner. Sylvia had dinner ready to put on the table. She was waiting for the girls to finish setting the table. Soon, she started putting the food into bowls, adding serving spoons and placing the bowls full of food on the table. Bud came in and sat down; he started yelling at the kids to get to the table, that dinner was ready.

Bud had no patience for Sylvia or the kids. He was itching to get started, and it felt to him as though they were all moving slowly to prevent him from starting his training. As everyone sat down to dinner, Bud kept picking on this kid or

that kid, trying to drive him or her away from the table. The kids sensed something was up with their father and that never ended well. Since they were not allowed to leave the table before they cleaned their plate, several of the kids took small portions. *Good*, Bud thought, *the sooner this is over, the sooner the training can begin.*

Sylvia sat down to eat and filled her plate from the various serving bowls. She was running a bit late for work, but the new place was closer to the bar where she worked. She was sure she could take the time to eat dinner and still make it on time.

As soon as Sylvia left, Bud gathered four of the kids outside the basement door, leaving Sharon inside alone. The kids had noticed the rabbits in the traps and were poking at them in interest. Bud yelled, "Stop that!" at the kids as he approached and caused the rabbits to freeze in the traps.

Bud grabbed the first trap, and the kids looked at him curiously. Bud set the trap just outside the basement door with the trap's opening facing into the basement. Bud opened the door to the trap and the rabbit ran out into the dark basement. As the rabbit ran frantically about in the small basement, one of the spring-jawed traps was sprung. SNAP! The trap closed and there was a brief squeal. Then there was dead quiet. Bud laughed aloud when the trap closed and turned to the next rabbit. Bud repeated the process and the results were the same.

Suddenly, Bud turned on the lights in the basement and picked up the traps with the rabbits in them. One was already

dead, and Bud tossed its carcass back into the woods. He then pulled back the trap with the live rabbit in it and let it scurry around the basement. He had the kids come into the basement and closed the door. He handed shovels to the two boys and told them to run the rabbit down and kill it with their shovel. He gave the girls the small spades, directed them to a corner of the basement, and told them to dig a grave for the rabbit.

The girls started to dig but stopped and ran back to the door, afraid of the chase that was happening around them. Bud yelled at them to get digging, but they were too afraid to move. Bud enjoyed the fear he could feel from the girls. *This is a good start.* he thought. George had tried to corner the rabbit in the basement, and because the rabbit was injured, it had slowed down. George stopped the small rabbit in the corner and prevented it from running around. Dick came up behind George and shouldered his way in front of him. George whispered, "Don't kill it! Just let it die." Dick picked up his shovel and struck the rabbit with the sharp end of the shovel one time. As George moved back away from the corner, Dick raised the shovel again and repeatedly struck the rabbit with the flat side of the shovel until it was still. After the rabbit was dead, Dick continued to vent his anger on the dead rabbit, striking it again and again. Bud enjoyed the fact that at least one of his kids appeared to have some balls, as long as he did not get any ideas.

It was getting late and Bud decided that training was complete for the day. The kids trailed back into the house in stunned silence. "That was fun!" Bud said to the kids and

laughed. "Did you think so?" The kids stood and looked at him for a long moment and then George said "No." Bud slapped George across the face and said, "What did you say?" He was standing over George with a clenched fist and waiting for his reply.

George looked at his father's fist then said, "Sure it was fun." Bud slugged George several times even though he had the response he was looking for.

Bud looked at the other three kids and each one replied "Yes." Laughing, Bud told the kids, "Good, because we are just getting started."

The next time they had training, the kids found that their father had kept the last rabbit in the cage trap and was feeding it. He was also slowly torturing the animal to death. Bud told the kids that they would have to help. He took a stiff piece of wire that he had sharpened to a point and put the wire through the side of the cage trap. He poked the rabbit with the sharp end of the wire, continued to corner it, and poked the rabbit until it bled. Bud stopped and told Dick, "I want you to come in here every day after school and poke the rabbit until it bleeds."

Bud had seen the fear on the kids' faces last time when he had the girls dig a grave for the dead rabbit. The rabbit carcass was still lying in the corner and smelled bad. Bud told the girls to get the small spades and finish the job they had started. Bud then turned to the boys and said, "Start digging two bigger holes; we are going to need them." The boys, afraid to ask, started digging.

Bud thought he could be patient while he sat there and watched the kids digging; he was extremely bored, however. He needed to generate some fear and excitement. He decided to leak his plans to the kids and gauge the effect. "I am planning some training sessions for you kids so that you will know what it feels like to die. This is just in case I have to kill you." Bud continued, "Remember, if you tell anyone, I will have to kill your mother and you too."

Bud noticed that the girls had completed the hole for the rabbit and told Susie and Gloria to go pick up the rabbit. Both of the girls cringed at the thought. Bud went to them and grabbed them by the arm, hard. He dragged them to the place where the dead rabbit lay in the basement. He forced each girl to touch the rotten carcass and then made Gloria pick up the dead thing and take it to the hole. Once Gloria had the rabbit in the hole, Bud made Susie cover the rabbit with dirt and fill the hole.

The boys were still digging and trying not to pay attention to what Bud was doing with the girls. It was difficult because the girls were crying and Bud was getting irritated with them. The boys had the sense to stay quiet, but the girls were too young to have developed that kind of control.

Bud decided that it was his time to have some excitement. He told Susie to lie down on top of the rabbit's grave. He said aloud to no one, "It already smells better in here." With that, Bud got down on his knees and then lay down on top of Susie. He laid his full weight on the girl and asked her if she would like to join the rabbit in the ground. Susie, crying, shook her

head no. Bud began dry-humping Susie to grind her body down into the dirt where the rabbit now lay. Bud told Gloria to climb on his back and help him. Gloria, believing that she had no choice, did as she was told. Once Gloria was on his back, Bud told Dick to pile on top and help. Dick climbed on top of Gloria and began to dry-hump her as his father had done to Susie. Susie began to have trouble breathing and could barely make a sound other than a very weak cry. Gloria was in pain from the weight on top of her, and she was crying loudly in Bud's ears. Bud told Dick to stop humping, telling him that it was hurting his back. Bud then told George that he was to get on top of Dick and add more weight to the pile. George, who had been watching the whole time, refused to get on top. He told his father that Susie could barely breathe and if additional weight was added, both girls might end up with broken bones. Bud finally looked at Susie's face and could see that her lips were tinged with blue. "You might be right, but that doesn't mean that you are not in trouble for disobeying me."

"Of course not," was George's only reply.

Bud decided that training was over for the night and walked out of the basement and into the woods. Bud needed to cool off and think. He had really received a charge from tonight's session, but it had not gone far enough. In addition, George was getting too old and too smart for his own good. He was setting an example for the others by not obeying him when he was told to do something.

He had forgotten about the agreement for George to take care of Sharon. Bud was trying to re-assert his power over all of the kids, but George was having none of it. Bud decided that George needed at reminder that Bud was in power. He was required to follow orders and keep his mouth shut, and Bud would make sure he understood.

The next day, after school was over and Sylvia had left for work, Bud took George out back and using his fists, gave George a beating. In order to get his father to stop hitting him, George agreed to keep his mouth shut about what was happening. George knew if he told, it would be his mother and the girls that paid the price. There was no one he could turn to for help.

Several weeks passed quietly for the Peterson household. The older kids went to school, did their homework, and stayed a quiet as possible. Their Mom was busy with work and their little sister, Sharon. It was relatively peaceful except that the kids could all feel their father building up to something. Bud was quiet, too quiet, and polite. The kids were unaccustomed to their father like this and did not trust it. They had heard an argument between their parents that included words like "divorce" and "take the kids." They could only hope; they could not trust in that either. They talked amongst themselves quietly; their greatest fear was that their father would kill their mother. If that happened, there would be no hope at all. However, hope they did, for the first time in many years.

Bud was very angry; there was talk, and Sylvia had told him. She said that some of her family had noticed bruises on

George and had tried to find out what was wrong. He refused to say a word except that it was not safe for him to talk. Sylvia had tried to talk to him herself, but without success. Bud told her that she was wrong; he would never hurt the kids, and he did not care enough about them to hurt them. Sylvia was shocked but knew that Bud had always been distant with the kids. She also knew Bud was one mean son of a bitch, but she had never felt threatened by him. Bud was able to convince her that he had done nothing wrong and told her to tell her family to butt-out.

Bud went into the basement to vent some of his anger at Sylvia's family, the Criders. He walked around the basement to release some energy. He pulled out a bottle he had secreted in the basement. He knew that booze was a bad idea when he was angry, but he felt helpless, and he did not like that feeling at all.

Now, looking around the basement, Bud stood over the two holes the boys had dug. The holes were rectangular and not too deep. They appeared to be the size of coffins and just deep enough for one to reach the top of the holes. This gave Bud a great idea! He had to be careful and not let anyone find out. This would work perfectly because he could cover any evidence of his activity by burying it using the dirt from the holes.

Bud looked around to see what he could find to work with. He tried lining the holes with the scraps of lumber in the basement. There were pieces long enough and wide enough to form walls on the holes, but they would not stay in place.

There were a few flat pieces that would work on the bottom of the holes, not perfect but doable.

Bud had enough scrap wood for three holes, but he wanted four holes. He removed the wood, and placed it against the side of the basement walls. He called the boys into the basement and asked them to dig two more holes, just like the ones they had already dug. Bud showed them how he had squared the sides and ends of the holes using a shovel. As he left, he said to the boys over his shoulder, "Oh, you don't need to make the new holes as long as the other ones, just about half as long should be fine." He added, "Make sure you are done before bedtime." It was winter and cold in the basement. Even though the ground was not frozen, it was a bit hard to dig.

Bud jumped into his pickup truck and headed to the lumber store.

Another week passed quietly enough, but the kids were on edge. The boys had been discussing the implications of the four graves they had dug in the basement. They were worried that their father had some evil plans. The kids were losing what hope they had, still too frightened to tell anyone.

The girls had not seen the four holes dug into the basement floor; they had been too afraid to enter the basement. After what the girls referred to as "the squishing," they had made a pact never to go down there again. They were worried they may be forced to go there again, very soon.

The following day, Bud was ready to begin his next training. He told all of the kids to meet him down in the basement; they headed outside to the basement's only entrance at the

back of the house. When they got to the basement door, they found it locked with a padlock. Bud walked up behind them; he unlocked the door and opened it for them. The kids saw that there was also a new hasp on the interior of the door.

After the kids had gone into the basement, Bud stepped inside and used the padlock to close the hasp on the inside of the door. Unsure why the change in locks and what to expect, the kids had a look of fear and disbelief on their faces. Bud laughed at their fear and said, "The lock is so that we won't be disturbed while we are training."

Bud turned to the girls; he told them to take off their clothes and wait until he told them what to do next. Gloria, having never been good in cold weather, stood crying and shivering even before she disrobed.

Both girls had seen the holes, two big holes and two smaller holes. Each hole had been lined with wood on the bottom and the sides. Looking around, Gloria could see no tops to fit the holes. The scene in the basement was terrifying to the girls. Both girls had been sure that, barring death, their father had done the worse he could to them. During the "squishing," Susie had been smashed so hard that it took her a while to breathe normally when their father stood up, finally taking his weight off. The girls exchanged glances to see if either one of them had any idea what would happen. They looked at their brothers. They both appeared as confused and afraid as the two girls did.

Bud told the girls to get into a hole. When the girls started to get into a big hole together, their father stopped them,

showing each one to a separate, smaller hole. He told the girls to lie down and the girls, watching each other, began to lie face down in their holes. This frustrated Bud, and he began to shout at the girls, calling them "stupid cunts" and telling them to "fucking turn over." The girls did as they were directed, feeling much more exposed and vulnerable lying with their faces up. Gloria was scared and angry; she did not like being called stupid, and she liked it even less to be called a cunt. She thought it unnecessary to use words like that. However, she was too afraid to say so.

Bud told the two boys to grab up a shovel. He had each one stand by a hole; George was next to Susie and Dick was over by Gloria. He told them to take a shovel full of dirt and toss it into the hole that each girl lay in. When the boys threw the dirt into the center of the hole, Bud told the boys to begin filling at the end and work their way up to the top.

Bud noticed that George was filling in the areas at Susie's sides and at her feet. He told him to get her feet covered faster so that he could move on. Dick was throwing dirt all over the top of Gloria below her waist. Occasionally, Dick would stop and move the dirt around the sides, adding more and then packing it down with the shovel.

A few times, Gloria felt the shovel hit her and she cried out. Bud walked over to the hole that Gloria was in and reached over to her face. Gloria threw up her arm to protect herself, because she thought that her father planned to hit her. Instead, Bud grabbed Gloria by her chin and turned her face to his. He took something out of his pocket and shoved it in her

mouth. Gloria was shocked when she realized that he had stuffed the handkerchief in her mouth that her Grandma Peterson had tatted for her so long ago. Gloria had searched for that handkerchief when they packed to move; she thought it was long gone. She had been saddened by the loss of something that her grandma had made special for her. Now, it was crumpled and filthy, stuffed into her mouth like a special punishment. Gloria wanted to cry at the meanness of the act, but she could barely breathe.

Gloria tried to calm herself, knowing that she needed to breathe to get out of the hole. Her brother continued to fill her hole, with her in it, tamping down the dirt. Gloria could feel the weight of the dirt on her legs and feet. When she thought no one would notice, Gloria wriggled her toes and feet. It helped, but only a bit. Dick was now filling in the area around Gloria's midsection, covering her abdomen and chest. It felt heavy and constricting.

Gloria looked over and could see that her sister was not as covered up as she was. It appeared as though Dick was working twice as fast as George was. George was moving much slower, and as Gloria watched, she could see that he was not filling his shovel as much as Dick was.

Gloria looked at her brother and said, in a whisper, "Slow down." He just looked at her and shook his head, then looked to see if their father had heard her. It was upsetting that her brother seemed bent on finishing first and would not slow down. She lay still, still checking her feet and toes, and once

her hands were covered, she started wriggling her hands to loosen the dirt around them.

Dick finished filling in around her midsection and Gloria's shoulders were next. It took Dick a few minutes to cover her so that only her head was now exposed. By packing the dirt as he went, Dick had filled the hole in such a way that there was not much loose dirt around Gloria's small body. Once her shoulders were covered, Dick turned to his father and told him that he was finished. Bud walked over and looked at the girl lying in the hole and told Dick, "You aren't done; you have to cover her head still." Bud said, "What I want you to do next is fill the rest of the hole and cover everything except the eyes, nose, and mouth. We will save that for last."

Gloria had been shrugging her shoulders, but that had only allowed her brother to pack dirt tighter around her upper body. When Dick began to fill in the areas around her head, Gloria tried to cry out. However, with the handkerchief stuffed in her mouth, her cry was too muffled for anyone to hear. Dick kept putting dirt around her head; he was careful not to get dirt in her mouth, nose, or eyes. He got down on his knees and added the last few handfuls of dirt with his hands, brushing the dirt away from her face. Almost done, he leaned close to Gloria and when their father was not looking, Gloria heard him whisper "Run!" to her.

Dick stood up next to Gloria, buried in her hole, and told his father that he was done. Bud looked over at George and told him to finish burying Susie so that they could get on with it. George was wary of their father's unknown plan and made

only a small attempt to speed up. George acted as though he was taking great care to do the work right, but he was really only trying to buy time.

Since Dick had finished burying Gloria, she had been unable to turn her head and see what was happening to her sister. Without any connection with her older sister, Gloria began to panic. She could suddenly feel that the weight of the dirt was much greater than she had thought. She began to struggle against the earth and free her hands. Gloria was having trouble freeing her hand, and no one could hear her cry out. Gloria felt a darkness overcoming her as her mind screamed out for help. Gloria fought the dirt and prayed for God to help her. She prayed that her mother would come and know what to do. Suddenly the darkness was complete; Gloria's mind was only functioning in survival mode. She had no idea what was happening, but instinctively, she knew that if she did not act, she would soon die.

When Gloria was next aware of what was happening, she was out of the hole sitting next to it. She was struggling to get to her feet and run but her body would not act. Her father and her brother were arguing, and Bud had just hit him in the face. Susie was also out of her hole, but she was standing. George had his shovel held in his hands, threatening to hit their father. Dick had picked his up as well and suddenly, their father was outnumbered. Dick looked at Gloria and told her to run again, and this time Gloria did. She ran outside the basement and paused to let her eyes adjust to the night sky. Susie joined her

a moment later, and they ran into the woods, hiding behind some trees near the edge of the yard.

Inside, the girls could hear their brother George telling their father that it was over. George told Bud that things had gone too far and he was going to tell their mother if he did one more thing to them. Bud tried to argue, but George was having none of it. He had made a decision and was sticking to it. Bud asked Dick whose side he was on and Dick simply said, "George is right."

Bud was angry, upset that the kids had called his bluff. He was going to have to reconnoiter and regain his power somehow. In the meantime, he needed to make sure that George did not tell their mother.

George got the girls and took them inside. He had the girls go to bed without bathing; he was afraid they would not be safe. No matter how dirty they were, a bath was not as important as keeping them away from their father right now. George now knew that their father was capable of anything, and he must act before it was too late.

The next morning after the girls went to school, Sylvia went into their room. As she started to smooth out their blankets and make their beds, she noticed all the dirt on their pillows. Stripping back the blankets, she saw that the sheets were also covered in dirt. Sylvia was determined to find out why when the kids got home from school. She waited for Bud to leave and meet his drinking friends. Knowing that Bud would not be back until late, when he figured she had left for work, she went to the school and took George out of class.

Walking out to the car with George, Sylvia told her oldest boy about the sheets she had found in the girl's room that morning. Sylvia asked him if he knew what was going on. He simply shrugged and started to cry. Sylvia drove away from home instead of toward it, figuring she had five hours or so before the other kids got home from school on the bus. Sylvia took drove George over the Kankakee River Bridge and into Knox. They got an ice cream and went over to a nearby park to sit down and talk.

Sylvia sensed that George, silent since she had asked the question earlier, was struggling with something. She sat with him in silence and waited until he was ready to talk. George's face was turning red again, and he clamped his lips shut in that way that always let Sylvia know that he was about to burst into tears.

"I don't know if I can tell you, Ma!" George blurted out. He cried again and cried so deep and so long that Sylvia's heart was breaking for her son. When he quieted, she asked him why he thought that he could not tell her. George said simply, "He said he would kill you." Sylvia asked him who had told him that and George shook his head.

Sylvia asked him, "Are you talking about your father?"

George nodded yes.

Sylvia told George not to worry that Bud might hurt her. She told him that if he was hurting any of the kids, he was already hurting her. Sylvia asked George why the girls' sheets were all covered with dirt. George answered, "I was afraid to let them take a bath because he was so angry." He sat there thinking

about the best way to let his mother know what had happened. He did not know how to describe what had happened. He was really just beginning to believe it himself.

George had gone to school that morning numb and not thinking clearly. He was more frightened of his father than he had ever been.

George eventually opened up and told his mother about the burials that had transpired last night. He told her that their father had been getting meaner and meaner all the time. However, he stopped there because he did not know how to admit that the abuse had been going on for many years, about the time that the baby had died.

Sylvia told George not to let on that he had told. She had a plan, and it may take some time to get it ready. George told her to hurry; he thought that maybe their father had plans to . kill one of them.

Sylvia and George went home and spent the rest of the day talking and playing with Sharon who was, thankfully, still too young to have become a part of all of it.

At home, things were getting bad between Sylvia and Bud. Nearly each night brought drunken arguments from Bud; Sylvia struggled to get enough sleep to drag through the seemingly endless days.

As winter became spring and then summer, Sylvia was on guard for any signs that Bud had begun hurting the kids again. She wondered if he knew what George had told her. When she asked George about it, he told her that his father didn't know that they had talked about what he was doing. George told her

that the way his father was acting was how he acted whenever he was bored. "It usually ends up with someone getting hurt," George said. Sylvia looked at her son and knew that she had to decide.

{ 20 }

Sunday at Grandma's

Grandpa and Grandma Crider had a huge house sitting on almost one hundred acres in Culver, Indiana. The house sat at the northwest corner of the property, away from the road. Crops were planted in fields to the south of the house, and to the east most of the property was woods.

The house was huge; it had two bedrooms off the kitchen and three bedrooms off the dining and living rooms. There was a screened porch running the entire length of the house along the west side of the home. The kitchen was big and laid out for maximum working space. My mother once told me that when they bought the land, the house had been unlivable. They spent one entire summer and fall fixing it up so that their family would have a place to live.

Next door, just north of Grandpa and Grandma's house, Uncle Rollie and Aunt Kitty had built their home. It was a smaller but well-kept house and became a safe haven for Gloria and Susie from time to time. Gloria would run over to see Aunt Kitty and Uncle Rollie when things were too much for her at Grandpa and Grandma's house. She and her sister al-

ways felt safe and special there; they knew they could trust Uncle Rollie and Aunt Kitty.

Spring was here and it would be summer soon. For the Crider family that meant getting the gardens ready and planning for Sunday family dinners. Soon, it would be time to start canning and freezing everything grown in the family gardens. Canning and preserving homegrown foods meant hours of working and cleaning up. That made for some very long Sundays for the women.

As each of Bill and Nona's grown children arrived, all with family in tow, Grandma Crider could be heard yelling out to Grandpa, "Bill go kill another chicken." Grandma always made sure that there was plenty of food. With all of the women helping in the kitchen and the men hunting and killing chickens, there was plenty of assistance getting things ready for dinner.

Depending on their ages, the grandkids spent time playing out in the big yard or just hanging out together and talking. Some of the older grandkids pitched in setting the big picnic tables or watching the food that was cooking on the big oil barrel grill their grandpa had made.

For Gloria, the trip from Hebron was always stressful. Not only was she car sick, but the car seats were covered in clear plastic, and the smell made her carsickness so much worse. It did not help that her father kept screaming at her and her brothers and sisters. He would threaten Gloria that if she puked in the car, he was going to "whip her ass." Gloria was not too worried about throwing up; her mom was there to

help. However, the atmosphere in the car was miserable, and it could be much worse on the way back home.

Susie and Gloria would run from the car as soon as they arrived. Immediately, the two girls would run to their Grandpa Crider and say hello. He always told each of the girls that they were his favorites as he hugged them tight, kissed their cheek. He would threaten to keep them sitting with him and then laugh and let them go as they got antsy to play with their cousins. The girls loved their grandpa and would have happily remained with him. However, there were many other exciting things to be done!

Gloria at five years old could not count how many people were there each Sunday. Now, Gloria was six and in first grade. They had learned to count to one hundred and up, and now she felt that she might be able to keep count of how many of her aunts, uncles, and cousins joined them at Grand-ma and Grandpa's house. She loved these days and felt so safe around her mother's family. Few things really bothered her. She was able to push them aside on Sundays at Grandma's and feel almost like everyone else.

However, things were changing for Gloria; she no longer felt safe anymore. She was not sure what was different inside, but she knew that she was very afraid, nearly all of the time.

It was nearly impossible to predict what might cause her to be afraid. Not just "scaredy-pants" afraid, but afraid she was going to blow up into a million pieces and die. When those moments came, Gloria could not talk; she could feel her throat closing and she had trouble breathing. The first time it hap-

pened, Gloria was walking down the steps into her Grandma Crider's basement.

As Gloria walked down the steps, she reached the landing and made the turn to take the last few steps to the basement floor. Suddenly, Gloria thought she saw something out of the corner of her eye. Sure enough, Gloria saw a decapitated head sitting on top of the laundry in Grandma's basket. She froze; she could feel her heart pounding in her throat. Gloria closed her eyes, thinking it might work to make the thing go away. When she opened her eyes, the head was still there. Hysterical and screaming, she headed back up the stairs. Her mother met her at the top of the stairway fearing that Gloria had fallen on the steps and hurt herself.

"The head! The head!" Gloria screamed; it made her mother's skin crawl to hear that screaming. "There is a head in the basket!" Gloria screamed again and added, "I can't go down there!" Sylvia looked at Gloria and could see how afraid she was.

Grandma Crider, a no nonsense sort of person, looked down the steps and said, "Gloria Jean, there is no head any-where in that basement! Now you just get yourself down there and get that jar of peaches I asked you to get." Terrified, Glo-ria held onto the doorjamb while her mother tried to get her to go down and look, so she could see that there was nothing there. Finally, her mother was able to coax her down into the basement by holding her hand and going with her.

As they made their way to the laundry, Gloria held onto her mother's hand and squeezed her eyes tightly shut. When

her mother stopped in front of the basket, she told Gloria to open her eyes and see that there was nothing there. Gloria could see that her mother was right, but she could not understand where the head had gone. Sylvia told her daughter to go back into the storage area and get a jar of peaches to take upstairs.

As Gloria proceeded to the back of the basement, she grew more afraid the further she got away from her mom. She bit her lip and took one careful step at a time, sure that the decapitated head was somewhere ahead. Finally, Gloria made it to the shelves of canned food. She grabbed a big jar of peaches and heard a noise behind her. She started to run, not planning to stop until she was up the steps. As she turned the corner, she nearly ran into her mom. She handed her mom the peaches and started screaming as she ran up the stairs to the kitchen.

She did not believe that the head was never there like her mom and grandma told her. She thought someone had moved it and was trying to scare her. She was sure that someone was in the basement too; she had seen shadows when she was down there. She was sure of it. Gloria did not change that belief until many years later. Her nightmares also continued for many years.

Sylvia knew then that something horrible had happened to that child in the basement. George had not wanted to elaborate when they talked, but he was scared. Now Gloria was acting more afraid than Sylvia had ever seen her. She was certain that she needed to make a plan to leave Bud. She was not sure that she could do it on her own, but she knew that her family

would help. When Bud was out hunting with the men, she talked to her sisters, Helen and Bev. She also talked to her best friend and sister in law, Kitty, who was married to her brother Rollie. She asked them not to tell anyone just yet; she did not want word to get around to Bud or his sister, Marge (Pete) who was married to her brother Blackie.

However, families being families, it was not long before her brother Rollie confronted Sylvia. He was worried; he said things had not felt right to him for a while. Now, he said, Kitty told him about Sylvia's concerns. Add to that, he said, "Gloria has begun acting differently. I cannot put my finger on it, but something is wrong there."

"Yes," Sylvia agreed, "and none of the kids will talk about it."

Rollie asked his sister if she would like to talk about this the following Sunday after dinner at Bev and Walt's house. Sylvia said, "Yes, but what do I tell Bud?"

Rollie said to Sylvia, "Bring Bud and the kids; I will take care of everything."

As the oldest Crider brother, it was Rollie's prerogative to call family meetings, so he let the brothers and sisters know that there was going to be a meeting at Bev and Walt's house the next Sunday. He did not answer any questions about it, saying it was about some of the kids; he added that no one should bring it up to Bud or Marge. Rollie talked to his brother Blackie about what was going on. He also told him that he was welcome to come to the meeting but only if he could

leave Marge and the kids at home. Blackie knew what it was about and told Rollie that he would be there.

On Sunday at dinner, all of the adults were a bit subdued. If anyone asked what was wrong, some just put it off to being tired from a busy week; others blamed the heat and humidity of the week.

Afterward, all of the families met over at Bev's house. As their car pulled into the yard, Bud said, "Ok, what the hell is this about?" Sylvia feigned ignorance and got out of the car. She had driven over, and Bud was pissed because he wanted to get home. Sylvia and the kids went to the door. Bud sat in the car fuming; she had taken the keys with her. Bud could see Blackie's car, Helen's car, Harold's car, Rollie's car. The "whole damn Crider clan" was here from what Bud could see. Except, he thought, Bob and Jim, both of whom lived too far for a late meeting.

Inside, Helen took all of the kids into the living room and got out the games. She told the kids that the parents would be talking in the kitchen, and they were not to be disturbed. Closing the door to the kitchen as she entered, she asked no one in particular, "Now what the hell is this all about?" All three of the Crider girls were small, none as tall as five feet and very petite besides.

Rollie looked at Sylvia and said, "This is your meeting, you go ahead." Sylvia sighed and squared her shoulders. She looked at her brothers, sisters, and in-laws; she simply said, "Bud has been hurting the kids." Sylvia let go of a breath she did not realize she had been holding for a long time. She felt a

weight lifting off her that she had been carrying and felt lighter as she looked around the room at her family. She had not felt this loved or cared for in some time.

Walt looked at her and shook his head in agreement, "Yeah, I saw some bruises on all of them that made me wonder."

Harold asked, "Just what has he been doing? Are you sure?"

Sylvia looked at them all and answered, "I am not entirely sure. All I know is what George told me and that was not much. He told me that he was afraid that his dad would end up killing one of them soon." She told them, "That is all he would say and he was so scared! I have never seen him like that. Gloria is acting very strangely, too; she is afraid of her own shadow and that has never been like her," Sylvia said.

"What are your plans?" Blackie asked her. He recalled the argument that Sylvia had with his wife, Marge. Marge had beaten Gloria during her stay while Sylvia was in the hospital having the baby. She and Marge were still not talking over that.

Sylvia looked at her brother apologetically and said, "I am going to confront him and if it is true, I am going to divorce him. You know, Blackie, it just isn't right for grown people to hurt children that way."

Blackie looked at his sister and then at his brothers and brothers-in-law. "You stay here;" he said. "All of us men will go out and confront him." Knowing that Bud had quite a bit to drink, Rollie went out to the car and walked up to Bud's win-

dow. "Get out;" he told Bud, "we have to talk." Rollie stood back as Bud out of the car and closed the door behind him.

"We have noticed that your kids may be in a bit of trouble," Rollie said, not quite knowing where to start.

"And how is that any of your business?" Bud shot back.

Blackie and Walt walked in closer and Blackie said, "It is our business because Sylvia is our sister and those kids are our family."

Bud turned to Blackie and said, "Fuck you! Those are my kids, and you cannot tell me what I can or cannot do to them!" Bud took a swing at Blackie and Blackie stepped back, letting Bud lose his balance.

Walt, angry at the thought of Bud hurting those kids, stepped forward and hit Bud with an uppercut to his gut. "You bastard, I heard stories about your father, but I did not think you would be the same mean son of a bitch that he was. You told me the stories yourself, just to gain my pity." Walt hit him again and Blackie stepped in to take a shot at Bud's face. "Now you can walk around with bruises just like the ones you put on your kids."

Then, just as Rollie was about to step in and give Bud a taste of his fists, Harold stopped him. "We should stop and talk for a minute, let Bud know how things stand."

Bud looked at the others and said, "Things will stand how I say they stand, stay the fuck out of my business!" With that, Rollie punched him in the nose and Harold punched him in the kidneys when he stood back up.

"Listen," Blackie said to Bud, "this is where it stands for you right now. My sister tells us that if you put one finger on her or the kids, she is leaving you. You should know that she has our support; we will help her get out and divorce you. We will call the police and have you arrested."

Rollie added, "If we see any more bruises on the kids or Sylvia, you will pay big for it, no matter what the court decides to do to you, do you understand that?"

Bud stared hard at the group and without a response, he laughed and got back into the car. "I am not the one who will pay for this; I will make sure of that."

He shouted over his shoulder, "Tell Sylvia to get her ass out here with the kids."

Rollie walked over to the open window and said, "Just remember what we said; no more bruises or we will come after you." Bud rolled up the window and Rollie walked back to the house.

Inside, Sylvia waited to hear what had happened. Blackie sat down, looked at his sister and said, "He is one mean son of a bitch, just like his father. He thinks that he is entitled to do just as he pleases. George may be right; you had better be ready to get out."

The ride home from Knox to Hebron was tiring. The atmosphere in the car so tense you could cut it with a knife. Bud kept turning to her, furious at her for having gone to her family for help. Several times, he shook his fist in rage at his wife and dared her to talk. Sylvia knew better; she was not going to allow him to drag her into an argument. Thankfully, all of the

kids were asleep except George who sat up, unable to sleep with all the fear and tension around him.

When they got home, Bud tried to start an argument. Sylvia just let his anger roll off her back, feeling strangely safe and powerful since her family had come to her defense. After a week, giving him time to cool off, Sylvia stood her ground and told him that she would take the kids and leave him if he touched any of the kids again. He smirked, unable or unwilling to concede power to anyone.

Soon, summer would be ending and so would weekends at the Crider family home. School would soon begin for the next year and preparations needed to be made. Things seemed quiet enough at home to Sylvia. She was almost lulled into believing that nothing she had wondered about was real; Bud was quiet except for the occasional argument and George had not brought up the basement again.

Bud could be patient, he decided. Once Sylvia stopped asking questions about the kids, she would feel safe again and stop worrying. Then he would be ready.

{ 21 }

Mom Makes A Run For It

Sylvia was aware that, despite his denial, Bud was still planning something. He was drinking heavily and trying to keep the peace. Sylvia had that feeling of walking on egg-shells that meant things were not as they seemed.

As the kids returned to school, Sylvia began to build her plan. She was getting up early, taking Sharon with her; she would drive out to her mom and dad's several times a week. It was wonderful to spend time with them; it just gave her an uplifting feeling to be away from Bud.

Finally, one day, her mother looked at her and asked, "Sylvia Mae, what is going on with you? I know something is up because we haven't seen you this often since you were married."

Sylvia sat at the table and put her head in her hands. "Mom," she began, "I have to figure out how to leave Bud and get the kids somewhere safe. Bud has been hurting them."

Nona looked at her oldest daughter and asked her, "Are you going to have to move away?" Sylvia told her mother that she was not sure where she would go yet, but she thought moving away would be safest.

Nona told Sylvia, "Write a letter to your Aunt Rose; she has her own problems, but she loves you and will help you get settled." Sylvia thought that Florida might be a good idea; it was far away and he would be unlikely to find her there.

She told her mother that she would write her Aunt Rose and then laid out her plan, so far, for her mother. She told her mom that she had been saving up what tips she could, and that her boss, knowing she was leaving, was giving her an extra twenty dollars on good nights. Sylvia walked over, got her purse, and sat back down at the table. "Mom," she said, "could you hang onto this for me so that Bud doesn't steal it from my purse?"

Nona walked Sylvia into her old bedroom and they hid the cash in her old bureau. Nona then called Bill inside and turning to Sylvia said, "It is time you told your dad what has been going on."

Bill sat down at the table and Nona brought him a cup of coffee. "Dad, I am going to have to leave Bud and move away to keep my kids safe."

Her father looked at her and he admitted that Rollie had told him something about it. He said, "I was wondering when you would get around to telling us; you have been hanging around here for a couple of weeks like you were ready to burst." Her father added, "Look Sylvia, I had heard stories for years about his father and when he died, the talk died down. I have always wondered how his sweet mother could have put up with that cruel bastard."

Sylvia agreed silently. She told her parents that she was planning to leave after school broke for Thanksgiving, traveling while the kids were out of school. "That way," she said, "the kids will not miss any school. I should have enough saved up by then."

Bill looked at his wife, who nodded, and told Sylvia, "Your mom and I have some saved up from last year's crop. We can pitch in some to help; I think we can afford one hundred dollars." Sylvia began to cry, knowing that her parents understood. She stood up and went to each of her parents, hugging them and crying harder. She was thinking of all the wonderful things that she and her children would have to leave behind to escape to safety.

Sylvia was carefully biding her time. She kept making regular trips out to her parent'' farm. She would always place what cash she had saved in the bureau. Sometimes, there would be a letter from Aunt Rose. She was anxiously waiting for Thanksgiving; she was planning a nice Christmas for Sylvia and the kids. Rose's daughter and her family would be there too. She had found a friend of hers named Shucksie to watch Sharon while Sylvia worked. Sylvia was grateful for her support and loved her for it. Her aunt could be scary to kids, but she was very much a Christian woman who abided no swearing and no alcohol.

Sylvia would write her back, updating her plans. Finally, when she knew that she was ready to firm up her plans, she let Aunt Rose know when she would be leaving Indiana and when she could expect her and the kids if all went smoothly.

Rose had told her to pack only lightweight coats and clothing; no winter wear was necessary in the warm Florida winters. That worked fine since it allowed Sylvia to take the kids' clothes to her parents' home a little at a time and store it in boxes in the basement. The only time Sylvia was even worried that Bud might find out was when they were all together at her parents' house for Thanksgiving. Things were still tense between Bud and her family, but in order to carry out her plan, he must not suspect. Sylvia's family was polite and welcoming to Bud, treating him as though the beating they gave him had never happened.

Sylvia had not even told the kids given the fact that the kids stood to lose the most if Bud found out.

The morning finally came; she had everything she needed in place. Bud left to hang out drinking with his friends, and it was time to get the kids in the car. Sylvia told the kids to get dressed and get into the car. She told them that they were going to visit Grandpa and Grandma Crider for a while. It was still early enough that she could make it out of Indiana if she hurried.

Sensitive to Sylvia's need to get on the road, Bill carried all of his daughter's boxes out to the screened porch. He looked at the meager amount of possessions his daughter was leaving with for her and the kids. It broke his heart to think of them all alone without family. He thought she would be better off; she had lived for nearly fifteen years with less.

As Sylvia pulled into her parents' driveway, she steeled herself for a tough goodbye. It was time to tell the kids where

they were going and why. She thought she had prepared herself for leaving, but it was harder than she thought it would be.

Her dad and the boys helped her pack the few belongings into the trunk. She added some extra diapers for Sharon and closed the trunk. Sylvia had the children say goodbye to her parents. So far, only the boys suspected something was up. As Susie and Gloria got into the back seat, Sylvia took the baby from her mother and put her on the front seat. She told George to sit in front to help her with the baby; Dick was to sit in the rear seat with the girls.

Sylvia got the kids settled and her dad handed her the one hundred dollars they had promised her. She added it to the other money in her purse, and her mom gave her another one hundred dollars as well. She hugged them and cried, thanking them for all of their love and support. She wished them a Merry Christmas and got into the car. She hoped that she would see them soon. She looked back in her rearview mirror to see her dad holding her mom, and watching them brought fresh tears to her eyes.

Sylvia started their journey, heading south from her parents' home to their destination, Sanford, Florida. Sylvia figured that she could make the trip in two days if she really wanted to push it. However, with four kids and a baby, she thought she should just take her time. As they started down Highway 31 toward Indianapolis, Sylvia explained to the kids that they were moving to Florida. She explained that they were leaving their father. Sylvia told her kids, "If anyone ever

hurts you again, you are to let me know immediately." Sylvia told her kids they would never have to worry about their father ever again.

As Sylvia suspected, it would probably take an extra day to travel with the icy weather and five children in the car. She took her time as she drove south; she planned to transition to Highway 65 once she got to Indianapolis, then to Louisville. She was planning to stop in Louisville for the night to get some rest.

In the back of her mind, Sylvia was worried that Bud would follow her to Florida, making their lives more miserable than ever. However, she thought, in all reality, he could not care less about her and the kids. The kids were very quiet, only speaking up if they had to go to the bathroom or were hungry. As usual, Sylvia had packed sandwiches, carrots, and celery for the trip. It would not last beyond the first day, but Sylvia encouraged the kids to eat. Sylvia was not certain if the kids were lulled by the road noise into this state of perpetual quiet, or if they were consumed by their own thoughts and fears.

Sylvia focused on driving, negotiating her way, with the aid of a map, through Indianapolis, and headed south toward Louisville. The roads were slippery and not well developed in southern Indiana. Sylvia was accustomed to driving in snow and ice, so she just drove slowly and steadily, not using her brakes unless necessary. Three hours into the trip, Sylvia was tense and tired. She would be glad when the group reached Louisville and she could get a room for them all to rest. As

Sylvia continued, she drove onto a two-lane bridge that crossed the eastern fork of the White River, just north of Seymour, Indiana.

With her attention focused forward, Sylvia did not see the truck coming. Sylvia had slowed to cross the bridge because there was more ice on bridges due to exposure. About one-third of the way across, Sylvia felt a tap on her bumper. Grabbing her steering wheel, she was able to control her skid enough that she only hit the side of the bridge with the back corner of the car and bumper on the passenger side. Taking a moment to assess, she asked her children if they were hurt, and with only a few bumps, they all claimed to be fine.

Suddenly, George said, "Mom, he is here!" At that moment, the back door on the passenger side flung open and Bud pulled Dick out of the car by his arm. Sylvia was stunned; she could not understand how he could have caught up with them so quickly.

Bud was furious; he had received a call from his sister, Marge, letting him know about Sylvia's plan to leave him and take the kids. She had not known much; she had overheard Blackie talking to his mother on the telephone and only got that Sylvia and the kids had left about ten that morning. When she questioned her husband, he told her that he did not know any more than she was gone. When Marge pressed Blackie, accusing him of beating up her brother and causing the family to run away, Blackie told her to mind her own business and left the house for work.

Bud had headed right for his in-laws' home, fuming mad. As Bill came out of the house to greet him, Nona stopped on the stoop behind him. Bud demanded that the two tell him where Sylvia had taken his kids. Bill looked at Bud and said, "Sylvia thought it was best if we did not know; she wanted the kids to be safe."

Bud said to Bill and Nona, "I would never hurt my kids; I don't understand why she had to leave." Bud pretended to cry, but when he removed his hands from in front of his eyes, there were no tears.

Not one to mince words, Nona said, "I think we all know that you have hurt those kids before; I think Sylvia has plenty of reasons to leave you and protect them. Now get on out of here and don't bother us again." Bud, realizing that he was getting nowhere, thought about beating the two up, but decided against it. If he had any hope of returning his family to Indiana, he had better find them.

Bud got into his truck and drove away from the Crider farm. He thought hard about where Sylvia would go. Being a woman who was close to her family, he decided that she would probably go to family. Suddenly, he realized that Sylvia was most likely to go to her aunt's place in Florida. He knew, if he headed south, that he would catch up with Sylvia before long. The roads were icy and Sylvia always drove slowly on ice.

Sylvia looked at Bud and asked, "What the hell do you think you are doing? Go home, I have paid the rent for the month; you can stay there until you find a place."

"No!" was Bud's immediate response. "There is no fucking way you are leaving me with my kids. I will not stand for it. I am taking the boys with me in my truck and you will follow me."

Sylvia looked at her kids; she knew she would have to do what Bud told her for now. She would look for another opportunity to leave when it was safe again. Resigned, she told him that she had planned to get a room in Louisville for the night. Bud told her to follow him and he would find a hotel. Susie had moved up to the front seat to hold the baby while Sylvia drove. All of the girls were crying. Sylvia turned to her daughters and said softly, "I am so sorry girls; I know that I promised you that you would never see him again, but he has your brothers. I cannot leave the boys with him; I will figure it out once we get to Florida."

Bud pulled back out onto the road and Sylvia pulled in behind him. Bud could feel the fear from the boys; it filled him with a sense of power he had not felt in a long time. He was enjoying the moment. Also good was the striking of the car his family was in, not knowing if it would crash through the railing and into the river below. He loved that kind of dangerous excitement. He was on the fence about which way he hoped it would go. *Good enough*, he thought, *for now.*

157

Bud drove the rest of the way in silence except to say to the boys, "Whichever one of you told will pay; you just think about that."

It took another hour and a half to reach Louisville and another forty-five minutes to find a room. Sylvia gave Bud enough cash to register and pay for the room. While he was in the motel's office, Sylvia took most of the cash she had on her and hid it in several places. Some she put under the trunk liner, and the rest she pushed up under the seat springs under her seat. She reserved just enough in her purse to pay for meals and gasoline.

It was going to be a long trip to Florida with Bud in tow. She was going to use more money than she planned, with another mouth to feed and another car to fuel. After dinner, she asked Bud, once again, to leave and go back home. She told him that even if he did not hurt the kids, she was finished with their marriage, the drinking and the not working. She told him that she could do much better on her own with her kids and they would all be happier.

Bud was not going back; he would not be able to face his mother and Sylvia's family. He was not going to let Sylvia get away with this; he would do what it took to stay with her and the kids. Until, that is, he could get some payback and take off. He told Sylvia that he would think about it and let her know in the morning before they left the motel. Sylvia, worn out from her day, agreed and went to bed.

The next morning, Sylvia and the kids grabbed some breakfast to go from a nearby diner and took it back to the

motel. She had told the kids that their father might go back home and they would go to Florida together. She told them to be quiet and stay out of his way if he got mad.

When they returned to the motel, the kids sat down on the floor and ate breakfast. Their mom and dad sat at the small table near the window to eat. Everything was quiet as the group finished breakfast. Sharon, two years old by this time, took the longest and Bud began to lose patience. He finally told Sylvia that he had decided to return to Indiana; he would say goodbye to them in the parking lot.

Sylvia had the kids get their belongings together and took them out to the car. She stayed in the room cleaning Sharon up after she finished her breakfast. Grabbing the few things that she and Sharon had, Sylvia went out into the parking lot to leave. She was stunned to find both of the boys back in Bud's pickup. She went to the passenger door and opened it. She told the boys to get into the car so that they could get on the road. The boys sat frozen; their father had told them that their mother did not want them to go to Florida. He told the boys that they would be returning to Indiana with him. Bud came around, closed the door, and grabbed Sylvia by the elbow. "These boys are going with me where ever I go; if that isn't Florida, then it will be Indiana," he said in a low voice so that the boys would not hear.

Sylvia stepped back from Bud and said loudly, to be sure the boys heard her, "I am not going anywhere without my boys, so I guess you might as well go to Florida." For the next

few hours, both cars headed south to Nashville, then toward Atlanta.

The second day, the group made better time south through Kentucky, into Tennessee and on to Georgia. The tension was palpable each time they stopped. No sense of excitement existed now, no anticipation of somewhere new. The kids had stopped talking yesterday and kept quiet all day the second day as well. As the two vehicles filled with Petersons approached Chattanooga, Tennessee, Bud signaled Sylvia that he wanted to stop. He pulled off into the parking lot of a roadside stand that served BBQ sandwiches. Everyone got out of the car and truck to stretch their legs, and Bud walked over to look at the menu. Sylvia asked the boys if they were okay. George and Dick shrugged their shoulders and Dick said, "All he does is talk to himself and laugh out loud; it is weird." Sylvia wondered just how far Bud would go, and she worried that he may have plans to hurt them all. The decision he had made, bumping the car on an icy bridge, was dangerous and hardhearted; they had been lucky she was able to control the skid.

Bud came back over, and giving the boys a hard look, told Sylvia that they would pick up supper now at the roadside stand. Sylvia agreed. It was a bit early, but the kids were hungry and could use the break. All of the kids seemed hungry, except for Gloria, who was suffering with an upset stomach from the car ride. Sylvia looked at the menu and told Bud to order Gloria a grilled cheese sandwich, one of her favorites. Bud refused, saying that they would all eat whatever he decided to order and got a twenty-dollar bill to pay for it from

Sylvia. Not looking for an argument, she relented, figuring Gloria could just not eat until later if she did not feel well.

Bud came back with the food and drinks for everyone, and they all sat around a large picnic table. Sylvia sat with Sharon standing next to her on the seat or in her lap while she gave French fries to the toddler. She would break off small pieces of her sandwich and gave them to Sharon who was ignoring them in favor of the fries. Everyone was hungry and dug into their food. After a bite, Gloria put her sandwich down and began to drink her soda pop and eat only the fries. Noticing that his sister was not eating her sandwich, Dick asked if he could have it. Before Gloria could hand the sandwich to her brother, her dad put his hand out and said, "No, Gloria is going to eat that."

Sylvia rose to Gloria's defense and told Bud, "She has had car sickness all day and should wait until later to eat."

Bud disagreed and said, "If she can eat French fries and soda, she can eat the nice sandwich I bought her." Gloria sat silently staring at her father; she was holding her lips together. Gloria had tried one bite of the spicy meat, and it had made her stomach hurt until she thought she might puke. Bud picked up the sandwich from Gloria's basket and pressed it to her lips.

Gloria sat stubbornly with her lips pressed together, refusing to let her father push the sandwich into her mouth. Tears were running down her face, and she was frightened that her father would hurt her again. Still, she refused to open her mouth or say anything. Bud got mad, and putting the sand-

wich down, he grabbed the girl's chin and tried to force her mouth open. Gloria pulled back and slid under the table, scrambling to get far enough away from her father so he could not touch her. Looking around, she found herself trapped by bars at the table ends and by all the legs at the table.

Suddenly, Bud grabbed Gloria by the shoulders and dragged her from under the table. Setting the girl on her feet, Bud took the sandwich and pushed it against Gloria's lips. "EAT!" he told the girl. Gloria closed her eyes and shook her head. She knew that if she opened her mouth to talk, he would shove the sandwich in her mouth.

Sylvia had stood up and came over to get Bud to stop, but he was not hearing her. She could not understand why Bud seemed bent on making an example of the child. Bud stopped trying to force feed the sandwich to her and instead threw it to the ground. He raised his fist, hit Gloria in the stomach, and said, "Now your stomach hurts, doesn't it?" Gloria opened her mouth and threw up all over the ground in front of her and Bud's shoes. Her father flew into a rage, certain she had done that to him purposely. He began slapping Gloria across the face and hitting her in the back when she cowered to protect herself from the blows.

Sylvia, stunned into immobility, finally found her feet and stepped between the two, trying to stop this crazy man from hurting her daughter any more.

Bud pulled back as he realized that Sylvia was now between him and the girl. He was sure that if he hit Sylvia, someone would call the police. He reasoned that no one cared

much if you beat your children. He understood that if the police arrived, he would wind up in jail, and Sylvia would take the children and leave him.

Gloria curled up in a ball on the ground and felt the pain of the blows her father had just given her. She hurt everywhere she could feel. Her father had hit her harder than she could remember him ever hitting her before. She began to cry, not because she hurt, but because she was giving up hope. She would never feel safe again.

The rest of the journey passed in almost complete silence. The group stopped for the night again as they got closer to Atlanta, Georgia. The boys rode in the truck with Bud, and the girls rode in the car with their mother. There was not much to say that would not be met with an argument from Bud, and Sylvia was deep in thought as she drove, trying to make a plan to get rid of Bud.

The last day of the trip was not long; they traveled from Atlanta to Sanford in just under five hours. As the car pulled into Sanford and found its way to Aunt Rose's, the kids could see their mother visibly relax.

Once they arrived at Aunt Rose's house, their mother told them all to get out and wait in the yard until she called for them. The boys jumped down from their seats in the truck and waited with their sisters until their mother came to get them.

Sylvia went inside to explain to her Aunt Rose how Bud had come to be with her. Rose looked at her and let her know that her parents had called to tell her about Bud's threats. She

told her that she should call her parents and let them know that they arrived safely.

Sylvia called her parents, and taking care because of the party line that they shared with the neighbor, she let them know that Bud had caught up to her and was there with her and the kids. She cut the call short, telling her parents that long distance calls were very expensive. She also wanted to wait until Bud was not around to talk.

{ 22 }

Great Aunt Rose

Great Aunt Rose's house was located at the end of a long paved road in Sanford, Florida. It was on a corner where the paved road ended and a dirt road began that went back several blocks. On the east side of the property there were citrus trees located in the front yard and all along the road to give shade to the one-story farmhouse they lived in. There were kumquat trees, tangelo trees, and orange trees. To the west of the house, Great Uncle Richard grew peanuts, and the kids would work in the summers to help him harvest the peanuts and other vegetables. Aunt Rose would sell the various citrus and produce at a stand just next to the porch at the front of the house. Several times when people would pull up at the fruit stand and Aunt Rose would go out to greet them. She would often return to the house waving her handkerchief in front of her face and commenting that the smell of alcohol had been strongly noticeable on a customer.

The house was a farmhouse in the true sense of the word, except that it was small. It had a long hallway kitchen at the back of the house and a screened-in back porch against the outside wall of the kitchen. There was a dining area at one end

of the kitchen. In the large living room, there was an area set to one side for a more formal dining area.

The rest of the room had a couch, armchair, and a rocking chair. A television was in front of the furniture, and to one side there was an end table where the telephone sat. The bedroom doors all entered from the living room as did the only bathroom.

Being a religious woman, Aunt Rose spent a great deal of time watching Bible Belt ministry programs like Oral Roberts. As a poor young girl of seven, Gloria watched in amazement one day as she telephoned and pledged a donation of $10,000 to the Oral Roberts ministry. Gloria thought to herself; *my family is part of the poor people that this ministry helps with that donation, why doesn't Aunt Rose give the money directly to our family?*

When the family first arrived in Sanford, Florida, they stayed at Great Aunt Rose's house. Aunt Rose worked for the telephone company for many years and was nearing retirement.

At the beginning, Uncle Richard was not living there, and the kids were unaware that Great Aunt Rose was even married. Later, they found out that her husband, Great Uncle Richard, was in prison. Rumors at the church where my aunt attended services revealed that Uncle Richard was accused of raping a young black girl. Aunt Rose steadfastly supported him and denied that the accusation was true, as did her daughter and granddaughters.

Aunt Rose was not expecting seven people to stay with her; she was expecting her niece, Sylvia and her five children. She was wary and unhappy when Bud showed up as well. She told Sylvia that she would have to get a place to live, Uncle Richard would soon be home, and there just wasn't enough room for all everyone. Aunt Rose was at work during the day, and Sylvia went about getting the kids signed up for school. She looked for a job every day and Bud was looking too. She figured that they both got jobs, there would be no problem finding a place to rent. However, when the kids returned to Aunt Rose's house after school, Bud would often be there drunk and complaining about their mom and Aunt Rose. If Bud weren't at the house, Sylvia would often go find him at a bar down the road and bring him home. The kids all just wished that he would stay at the bar.

Great Aunt Rose was a woman to be reckoned with. God-fearing, Bible pounding, and every bit of four foot nine, she had a dynamic about her that said *don't mess with me*. The kids were all afraid of her, even George at six foot four. The kids did everything she told them to do. They believed everything she told them.

Imagine the girl's dismay when they found out that Aunt Rose was wrong about Uncle Richard. Uncle Richard didn't like little black girls; he liked all little girls.

{ 23 }

The Truth About Uncle Richard

It was raining the day that Gloria walked into Great Aunt Rose's house. She saw a man she did not know sitting in Aunt Rose's rocking chair. Gloria walked over to the TV and turned it on so she could watch after-school cartoons.

The man asked Gloria's name, and when she told him; he said that it was nice to meet her and introduced himself as Great Uncle Richard. They were alone in the house, and he was sitting in the rocking chair covered up by a blanket.

Gloria's clothes were all soaked from the downpour she had walked home through. Uncle Richard said, "You look cold in those wet clothes. Why don't you climb up here under my blanket and get warm with me."

She looked at the man, wondering if she should do what he said. She was shivering from the cold and wet clothing. By then, she understood that she must do whatever an adult told her to do or there were consequences. As she climbed into his lap, she noticed that his shirt was off, it lay on the floor beside the chair; he grabbed my white dress and pulled it over my head. "Why did you do that?" she asked, "I don't like to take my dress off."

Uncle Richard replied, "I didn't want your dress to get me all wet again, and besides, it will be easier for us both to stay warm without clothes on."

She shivered and leaned back as he covered her with the blanket and said, "Okay."

After a few minutes, he started to rub her back, knees, and legs. She began to relax and feel warmer. Soon he began to massage her chest. As she tensed up, he shushed her and said, "It is okay, it is okay, just relax everything will be fine". Gloria was frightened of this big man and ashamed that she had allowed him to take her dress off, leaving her naked except for her panties.

Gloria felt him pick her up and turn her so that she was facing him. She pushed against him and squealed, unsure of what he was doing. Again, he shushed her and reassured her that he was just trying to get warmer as he pulled her panties off. As she sat down, he put one of her legs on either side of him through the arms of the rocking chair. Suddenly, she realized he did not have his pants on either. She began to cry and asked him to stop what he was doing. He placed his hand over her mouth and kept saying, "It's okay, it's okay, it will feel warmer soon, just relax." She struggled against him, but she was not strong enough to stop him. In the end, she did as she was told to do.

He placed his hands between her legs from behind. He put a finger inside her and touched her with another finger. He held her down against him with his arms wrapped around her back. He was rubbing against her with his body and rocking

the chair at the same time. Suddenly, he removed his fingers and replaced them with his penis. She began to hurt between her legs and started to cry, "Please stop, please stop, please, it hurts!"

He kept rocking and held her down for a few more minutes. All the time that he was rocking, he was holding her down on top of him. She felt pain between her legs as he tried to push inside of her. He tried harder and harder; the more resistance he felt, the harder he pushed. She was too small inside for him to enter, and it hurt. It hurt so badly, it felt as though he had pushed a hole all the way through her. In the end, he just wound up rubbing himself between her legs until she was all wet and sticky.

She got down, was ashamed of what had happened. She was ashamed because she was too small to stop him. After he was done, he pulled her dress over her head and told her to go clean up. He told her if she was bleeding, she should clean that up too and keep her mouth shut about it. He told her that he really liked what they had done and he would do it again sometime.

He told her that she could never tell anyone what he had just done or he would go to jail for a long time. "That would make Aunt Rose very, very sad," he said. Gloria did not want to hurt her Great Aunt Rose, so she did what she had been told to do and kept her mouth shut. Gloria made sure never to be alone with Great Uncle Richard again.

{ 24 }

Country Club Estates

It was much easier to avoid Great Uncle Richard once the girls banded together and made sure that they were never alone.

Soon, Sylvia had a new job. The kids were excited to move and to get away from Aunt Rose's house. There were things about being there that they loved. They loved to pick tangerines and kumquats or pull weeds for Aunt Rose in her garden. However, on the other hand, there was Uncle Richard.

One day, Uncle Richard coerced the older girls, Susie and Gloria, into working in his peanut fields with the promise of money. The fields were nearby but not in view of the house. He had offered to pay them to pick peanuts for Aunt Rose's fruit stand. He asked Gloria only, but when she invited her sister to go along, he relented. Uncle Richard sat on an upended bucket at the edge of the field and watched them work.

Both the girls were on hands and knees, digging into the soft, warm sand, pulling up the roots that held the peanuts from the ground. Concentrating on the task, the girls began to work their way in different directions. Since the girls had their backs to him, Gloria did not notice when Uncle Richard came

up behind her. She started when he spoke, "Let me show you how to do that." She looked behind her as he knelt down on the ground and began to dig his fingers into the sand. She did not see anything different in what he did, but pretended to try to concentrate and do it his way.

Suddenly, she was face down in the field, pressed into the ground as Uncle Richard threw his weight on top of her. "Stop," she cried, "you are hurting me!" He did not say anything; he began struggling to pull down her panties. She was moving so much, he wasn't able to get his hands under my dress, and he began cursing at her to stop moving. His weight was pressing down on her so heavy; she was having trouble breathing. Because of the sand, she began coughing. Getting frustrated with her struggles, Uncle Richard lifted his weight off her so that he could gain control and pull her panties down. She bolted out from under him, kicking back at him as she pushed away. He almost caught her foot to pull her back, but she kicked his hand and got away.

Susie became aware that something was going on, was running toward them. Gloria grabbed her hand and said that they should run to the house. When they got inside, she asked Susie why she had not come sooner. She told her that she could not see her where she was digging because the rows were too high. Susie said she was sure something was wrong when she could see Uncle Richard's butt up in the air. The girls both laughed and then remembered that they would not get the pay Uncle Richard had promised them.

When Uncle Richard walked into the house, he did not say anything to the girls. Gloria was surprised when she heard Susie ask him for their pay. He balked and said that they had not done enough work to be paid. Susie asked him if they should ask Aunt Rose for the money instead. He said nothing further; he just put one dollar for each of the girls on the table and left the room. One dollar was a huge amount of money to the girls. Soon, Sylvia found a house to rent, and the girls never had to worry about Uncle Richard again.

The new house was located in Sanford, in a housing tract called "Country Club Estates." It sounded nice, and the kids were excited to be moving out of Aunt Rose and Uncle Richard's place and into one of their own. Their mother had been working for a few weeks and had received enough in tips to make it work. Sadly, their father was still not working. Gloria heard her mother comment to Aunt Rose, "It is hard to find a job with your ass glued to a barstool." Gloria thought her mom did not really believe that Bud was looking for a job. Gloria had to agree with her mother; she was worried that if he never got a job, then he would never leave.

They loaded our belongings into the truck and Bud headed to the new house. They were not expecting what they found there. Country Club was the wrong name for the housing tract. The homes were made of concrete blocks and the floors were asphalt tile, not carpet. When anyone walked, footsteps rang loudly throughout the house. The kitchen held a stove and a refrigerator, as well as cabinets with a billion dead cockroaches inside. Susie and Gloria walked around, trying to decide

which room they wanted. They looked in all of the closets ran from the rooms screaming because of all the cockroaches that scurried away.

The girls were assigned a small room and their two beds were set up. They had found hundreds of dead cockroaches and refused to put any clothes in the closets or dresser. At night, they would lay awake waiting in case cockroaches would get on their beds. Eventually though, the girls had to sleep, cockroaches or not.

Gloria still had nightmares about the head in my grandmother's basement. A new nightmare also appeared during this period at least that is what her mind wanted her to believe. The nightmare was about Abraham Lincoln. Gloria would be asleep and suddenly find herself in the midst of a waking dream. She was aware that she was lying in her own bed, trapped underneath a very tall man who she thought of as Abraham Lincoln. She would be screaming and pushing on the man, and the next thing she knew, the tall black figure was running out of the door.

The Petersons did not stay at that house long, in fact the family moved quite frequently once they moved to Sanford. She never had the dream again once they moved out of that house.

{ 25 }

The Small Red Trailer

The family moved from the house in Country Club Estates after only a few months. Realizing that she had a lot to learn about Sanford rental homes, Sylvia had taken those months to find something more suitable.

The home she found was not far from Aunt Rose's house. It was down the dirt road that ran on the east side of her place. Down the street that ran behind her house were a collection of small homes and mobile homes mostly occupied by navy families. The mobile home that they moved into had a Florida room attached to the front of it. It was a tight squeeze, but it was far cleaner than the last place.

Susie and Gloria slept on the pull-down couch in the Florida room, the boys had the bedroom at the back of the trailer, and Sharon still slept in her parents' room. There were other families with kids, so the kids always had fun. Shucksie was caring for Sharon while mom worked, and Gloria would stay at her house after school as well. Susie, being older, was allowed to walk home and stay by herself. She was nine years old after all. Susie would walk Gloria to Shucksie's and then walk home to do her homework.

Some days, Shucksie would talk Susan into staying, telling her that Sylvia was working late. Everyone knew that Shucksie liked kids; she would make the girls peanut butter fudge and feed them. Shucksie had better toys than the girls had ever seen before.

Susie told Gloria that Dick had begun making her have sex with him. Dick, fourteen, told Susie that he was a man and needed sex from her. Gloria suggested to Susie that she should stay away from him until their mother was home by staying at Shucksie's house. She wanted to but was afraid that Shucksie would not want her there. Gloria talked to Shucksie and told her that Dick was being mean to Susie and hurting her. Shucksie agreed that it would be best if Susie stayed with her so from then on, she did. She tried to ask the girls more questions, but they just feigned ignorance. When Shucksie asked Susie, she told her that she did not want to talk about it.

Unfortunately, Dick only changed his game plan. At night, Gloria would wake up in the sofa bed she shared with Susie to find Dick on top of Susie forcing her to have sex. Dick threatened them both to be quiet so that their mom and dad would not find out. Eventually, one night, their parents walked out of their bedroom and ended that. Dick was mean and sullen for weeks until finally he figured out a place where he could make Susie give him sex again. Susie was quiet about it and seemed to have given up. She told Gloria that she had to give in to his requests for sex or he would beat her. She told her that he was as bad as their father and almost as mean.

They did not live there for long either. By summer, they had already moved on. However, it was at the new house that the girls made some good friends. Those friends came into their life again when they were older. The kids lived in a mobile home next door to the family; their names were Robert and Marcia White, two Navy dependents. We were not Navy dependents until my mother re-married several years later.

When they came into the girls' life again, all of the fear and shame rushed back to Gloria like a flood. The small kindness that Robert showed her was important to her after all these years they had been apart. He made her feel almost normal, important. Robert played the role of the big brother she should have had. Gloria was sure everyone knew her shame, she was fearful everyone would know It was decades before Gloria confronted those fears and eventually the shame that came along with it.

{ 26 }

Sharon's Reprieve

The first few years, the whole family had trouble adjusting to the hot and humid climate in Florida. There were days when the humidity was so high, it would sunshine and rain at the same time.

The area of Florida where they lived was only a forty-five minute drive to the beach. They always went to New Smyrna Beach, they allowed cars to drive down and park on the beach near the ocean. There was a bar nearby where their father could sit and drink while the kids played in the ocean.

However, trips to the beach were only on weekends when Sylvia was not working and those were few. On hot days, when the kids needed to cool down, they could walk to one of the local lakes and jump in. Some of the lakes were better; the kids preferred the lakes that had white sand bottoms. It was much easier to see what was at the bottom. Other lakes, littered with broken bottles, used car parts, barbed wire, and other metal parts, could make swimming dangerous.

The kids favorite lake was one called "Crystal Lake." The girls called it that because it was so clear that they could actually see the bottom way out in the deep part of the lake. They

liked swimming out to the platform, anchored forty feet out in the lake. It would take all of the girl's energy to get there, and they would lie on the platform and catch their breath.

Sylvia took take them there often. There were restrooms and picnic tables under shady trees, it was a nice place to go and have a picnic on her days off.

One time when the family went to the lake, their father went along. This was not completely out of character for him, but it was unusual. The kids had more fun when he was not there, but he had been making an effort to be nice. Bud was swimming with the kids and would chase them back into the water if they got out, laughing. Gloria would just try to avoid letting him touch her, it was never a good sign when he was nice, she did not trust him.

Susie and Gloria managed to avoid him a good portion of their time at the lake, except when he wanted to pass a beach ball and insisted that all of the kids play except Sharon (who was too young yet). As the game started, all four children stayed in the shallow water. Bud would throw the ball out further each time, insisting that the closest kid swim out to retrieve the ball and throw it back.

The kids found it incredibly difficult to tread water and toss a beach ball any distance, because the beach ball lacked the weight to gain any forward momentum. If one of the kids was unable to throw the ball all the way to him, he would begin calling them names and telling them what wimps they were.

Tiring of the beach ball game, Bud went into the lake and began wading and floating around to cool off. Sylvia asked him to take care of Sharon while she set the picnic table for dinner. Bud told her to bring Sharon to him, but she told him to get out of the lake and take Sharon, not wanting the child to get wet and cold.

Bud walked out of the lake and took Sharon from her, then turned around and went back into the lake. Sylvia was frustrated and told him to make sure that she did not get cold. Bud told her that everything would be fine. He held Sharon to his chest as he waded out with her. Sylvia was keeping a close eye on him, so he brought her into shallow waters and stood her down on her feet. Sharon could walk but still not sure-footed in water, so she fell on her butt a few times and cried. She held her arms up to Bud, so he picked her up and held her against his chest.

Bud was keeping track of Sylvia; he was watching to see if she was keeping track of him. He slowly made his way to deeper water with Sharon held high up on his shoulder. Each time the water got closer to Sharon's feet, she would make a distressed noise and take quick, sharp breaths. Once Bud reached a depth where he was just barely able to touch the lake bottom, he took Sharon off his shoulder and held her against his chest.

Bud knew that Sylvia was busy; he had been watching her. He was tired of taking care of the baby and losing patience with Sylvia. He rationalized that if Sylvia did not trust him, then he would give her good reason. Making sure that Sylvia

was not watching, he grabbed Sharon's feet with one hand and pulled her under. With his other hand, he pushed her under further and kept her there. At that moment, he heard Sylvia scream, "Where is Sharon?" Sylvia and George headed for the water and started to look for her. As they reached the edge of the lake, Bud pulled Sharon up out of the water. Sharon was coughing and struggling to get her breath. Sylvia knew that Sharon was okay when she began to cry. Sylvia screamed at Bud, "What were you doing, are you trying to kill the baby?"

Bud looked at her and laughed, "Don't get so wound up; it was just a joke! You kept watching me like you thought she was going to drown, so I let you think she did."

Sylvia was suspicious that Bud actually intended to let Sharon drown. He had only pulled Sharon out as she began to scream. "That is what you do with kids, Bud. You watch them closely so that they do not get hurt!" she yelled. Sylvia grabbed her daughter from his arms and, calming the child, realized that things were much worse that she suspected. All of the things she had suspected in the past were most likely true as well.

Knowing the effort Bud took to capture them when she left Indiana with the kids; she knew that she had to be careful.

{ 27 }

Snake Hunt

In 1963, the Peterson family had been living in Sanford, Florida for almost a year when they moved for the third time. They moved into a farmhouse outside of Sanford owned by Sylvia's Aunt Rose and Uncle Richard. The house was one and one-half miles from the highway where the bus stop was. It took the children a good half-hour to make the trek down the dirt road from the farmhouse to the highway and another half-hour back again at the end of each school day.

Things with Bud had been getting much worse. Gloria's brothers and sisters were as afraid as she was; they had all begun to lose hope. It seemed he would not spare them any pain. They were hoping that somehow, someone would get them away from the terrible person he had become. Gloria thought that she loved her father, (aren't you supposed to by law or something?) but she was afraid of him. Gloria was sure he didn't love her (isn't he supposed to by law or something?). She could sense only anger or cold nothingness from her father.

The house her mother rented from her aunt and uncle was a creepy, creaking old two-story house with glass doors at

every entrance. Huge, leafy trees shaded the entire west side of the house, and orange trees provided shade and citrus at the back. The driveway was on the south side of the home leading up to the screened front porch; the glass doors on that side of the house would slide open to let in cool air on sultry Florida evenings. To the east of the house, a garage stood with several rooms overhead. Beyond the house, yard, and garage, to the east were sandy fields where Uncle Richard planted his crops of turnips, collards, and mustard greens. He grew tomatoes, too; the children would on the swings and eat them straight from the garden. Ripe, red, and juicy, Gloria and her sisters bit into the tomatoes and let the juice run down their faces. Every bit of juice, seeds, and flesh from those tomatoes was a coveted treat for the girls.

The farmhouse seemed to have a life of its own. When there was a storm, lightning often found its way through the glass in the doors and struck the lower landing on the staircase. Contrary to the belief that lightning never strikes in the same place twice, it seemed that lightning always struck in the same area on the lower landing. It created a strange, glowing ball and static filled the room. It made the girls' hair stand on end. Gloria and her sisters held their breath, not daring to move, as if remaining motionless and not breathing would save them.

In that house, Gloria learned that she must never bathe during an electrical storm and never let anyone (or anything) know that she is not asleep. She had heard more than one

adult comment on how this house gave them the "creeps" and how it made "eerie" or "peculiar" noises.

Most nights, Gloria lay awake, frozen in fear, she could hear footsteps tread up the staircase and pause on the second landing where the stairs turned. Gloria and her sisters shared a "bedroom" that was really the final landing at the top of the stairway. Gloria covered her head and lay stiffly, feigning sleep and terrified as she heard something moving around in the room. Occasionally, she would peek out from under the blankets covering her head. She could see a big figure standing over her sister's crib next to the window. The figure loomed large and dark over the crib, its soft edges resembling a furry animal reared up on its back legs. It hovered near her sister; Gloria could hear it breathing. She pulled the blankets back over her head slowly and quietly. Soon, she felt something put its hands on her body; she was never able to remember what happened the next day. She could only recall the weight of those hands on her body and the terror as blankets were pulled from her clutching fingers.

There were storage closets built into the walls on one side of the landing. These attic closets were bigger than the landing the three girls shared as a bedroom. The closets were full of trunks and boxes, but there were small spaces where one could try to hide. In those storage closets, Gloria would learn some very frightening and painful secrets. The kinds of secrets no seven-year-old should know.

On long summer days, Gloria often sat out on the swing set in the backyard and watched the workers picking and sort-

ing the foods that Uncle Richard grew. She was born and raised in northern Indiana and required a translator each time one of the Negro workers asked her a question in their heavily southern-accented voices. The word orange sounded to Gloria like "arrgge," and each time they asked she would reply, "What?" The dark-skinned women would then repeat themselves, getting louder with each repetition. Thankfully, her oldest sister, Susie, had no such incapacity and came to her rescue as Gloria stood there frozen, afraid of the person asking. Susie would say to her, "for Christ's sakes, Gloria! They only want to know if they can have some oranges!" She would tell the people to go ahead and pick the oranges they wanted.

Gloria and her sisters spent a lot of time exploring the nearby woods, creeks, and fields. Weekdays, when they walked to or from the bus stop at the highway, they would encounter long black snakes. These snakes were hooded, like cobras, and would rise up off the ground and chase after rabbits and rodents along the creek bank next to the dirt road. Being very young and from Indiana, the girls had never seen snakes that could do such a thing. Fascinated and frightened, they decided they were very scary snakes, these Black Racers.

One time, late for the bus, Susie and Gloria decided to run down the dirt road to the highway. It wasn't long before the black snakes noticed the girls, who apparently found them just as fascinating as their prey. After that day, when the girls noticed one of the snakes watching them, they would run away

terrified. Only later did the girls realize it was the running that attracted the snakes' attention.

One day, as a warm Florida summer day became hot, Gloria and her youngest sister, Sharon, sat playing in the sand. The palmettos swayed, surrounding them in a breeze and cooling the sweat from their bodies as they disturbed a doodlebug in its burrow. The girls would drop grains of sand on the conical opening to the tiny burrow and watch with interest to see if it was enough to cause the bug to kick the sand up. There was not much to do on a summer day in the small Central Florida town; everywhere was too far to walk, and they were too young to go alone.

As they played in the sand that day, the girls saw their father approaching with a gun. The girls exchanged a quick look of fear. Gloria knew that meant something bad was about to happen. It was too late for her to take Sharon and run and hide; he had already seen them. If he caught up to them, Gloria realized, it would be much worse in the end.

Bud Peterson was angry; he followed his wife, Sylvia, to Florida over a year ago and nothing had changed. His wife still thought she could leave him and take the kids. She was threatening to do just that, again. Bud had decided that he needed to prove to her that he was the one in charge. He believed he had figured out a way to let her know her place.

Roughly a year ago, she had taken the kids and left Hebron, Indiana to get away from him. He figured out her plans and caught up with her before the end of the first day of her trip to Florida. He had guessed she was heading south because

she had some relatives down in Florida; it made sense to him. It hadn't been difficult for him; she'd left in December; with all of the bad weather, icy roads, and five kids, it had been slow going. When he caught up to her, he had forced her car into a spin on an icy bridge by tapping the back bumper on one side with his truck. The car had struck the side of the bridge, but it was a slow spin and no one was hurt, not much anyway. He was angry enough he had hoped to hurt at least one of the kids. When the car slowed and stopped, he had taken the two boys, George and Dick, into his truck and made them ride with him to keep Sylvia from taking off. He left the frightened girls in the car with their mother; he did not want to listen to their sniveling. Sylvia was at least smart enough to keep her mouth shut and not let on to the kids.

He couldn't stand the brats, didn't even want them back, but that was not the point. No one was going to leave him like that; those kids belonged to him to do with as he pleased. If Sylvia only knew the half of it, she would have his ass hauled off. He would have to make her get in line just like the kids.

Bud believed all females to be worthless, and he would not be convinced otherwise. His own mother had stood there quietly while his father had beaten him and his siblings senseless. He relished the memory of hearing her screams of pain when his father took to beating her after all of the kids had left home. He and Sylvia lived in the apartment behind his parents' duplex when they were first married. Some nights the screaming got so loud that it would wake Sylvia up, and she would make him go and check on his mother. He would go

downstairs and watch as his father beat his mother, stopping him only when it appeared he might injure her badly.

Now I'm going to have to show these brats just who is in charge, Bud thought. It was time to send them all a message; they needed to understand that he would deliver on his promise. *Damn it, anyway. Those nosey ass relatives of my wife started all of this trouble by asking too many questions.* He had taken quite a beating from two of her brothers, and he was still mad as hell about it. Yes, he would show them all.

Bud walked up to the girls and said, "Let's go for a walk and see if we can find some snakes." Both of the girls' eyes grew round with fear, and Bud laughed aloud. He liked it when they were afraid; it meant they would do anything he told them to do.

He had been thinking recently that these two were really more trouble than they were worth. Hell, he had never asked for five kids, just the first one was more than he ever wanted. These two were the smallest, small for their age really, and if something happened to both of them, it would be a lot easier to explain. There would be questions, but nothing he couldn't handle. So far, he had gotten away with many things, mostly because people just refused to believe that anyone could be as creative as he was. They all thought that anyone who would do the kinds of things he liked doing to kids must be crazy. In addition, crazy was something that they think they know on sight. Not one of them was as smart as him, not even these kids. Kids are stupid by nature and prone to doing stupid

things, like stepping on a coral snake, copperhead, or rattler. On the other hand, something much worse might happen.

Bud said to the girls, "Walk ahead and look for snakes. I will hang back and when you see a snake, I want you to holler 'SNAKE!'" The younger girl, Sharon, started crying softly; Gloria put her arm around her sister's shoulder and whispered something into her ear. She quieted almost immediately. Bud thought to himself, *that one is at least smart enough to know when to keep her mouth shut.*

As they continued the snake hunt, Gloria knew how mad their father would get if they cried, and she warned Sharon not to cry or he might beat them. Suddenly, Bud began to laugh at the girls because he knows they were frightened, and the sight of the little one crying had stirred him up; he was ready for more excitement. Soon, both girls began to laugh as well in an effort to appease their father. Gloria thought to herself, *this must be what crazy feels like* as she laughed, tears streaming down her face. Bud screamed at them to shut up. The girls quickly got quiet and started to walk again. Gloria could feel the pain as she shoved her tears down; they were now a big, hard lump in the middle of her chest.

The three walked for a while down a footpath through an overgrown area sure to have some snakes or at least critters. There were overgrown palmettos and pine trees on each side of the hot sand path. Gloria could feel the hot sand on the soles of her bare feet and worried about Sharon, whose feet were not nearly as tough as her own were. She considered

carrying her little sister but knew that they may need to run from their father and decided better of it.

Between some of the bigger pines, huge black, red, and yellow jumping spiders had woven their webs and were waiting for prey to venture too close so that they could pounce on it. Jumping spiders would also leap if startled, and the girls had always been afraid to walk too close to the webs. Gloria kept thinking to herself, *Red on black. . . friend of Jack. . . Red on yellow, kill a fellow.* Gloria was more afraid of the coral snakes, rattlers, and moccasins than the spiders. However, moccasins were water snakes, and they were nowhere near water.

Both girls were choking back tears, and Bud was becoming more excited by the moment as he worked up the courage for what he was planning to do next. He let the girls walk out farther in front of him to put some distance between them. Suddenly, Bud raised his shotgun to his shoulder, aimed, pulled the trigger, and shouted; "SNAKE!" at the same moment.

Both girls felt the blast of birdshot as it flew past. Sharon was hit in the leg by several pellets. As Sharon began screaming, the girls' oldest brother, George, crashed through the brush and yelled at his father, "What the hell are you doing?"

His father replied, "There was a snake; it was going to bite one of the girls." George was fifteen and as tall as his father, if not as big. George didn't believe it for a second; he had followed them into the woods and suspected that their father had bad intentions.

George grabbed up the youngest girl and grabbed Gloria by the hand. He realized then that Sharon had blood running down her leg and that she had been hit. Sharon was still screaming; Gloria thought to herself, *Sharon may be a bit crazy.* George asked Gloria if she had been hit. Still in shock, she told him, "I don't think so, nothing hurts." When he turned her around, George could see that there was blood on her forehead and a small gash around her hairline. George knew that Gloria had been hit but also that she could not see anything because she had recently lost her glasses. Using her poor eyesight to his advantage, he wiped the blood from her forehead with his hand before it got into her eye. He thought that the wound looked superficial and saw no hole where birdshot might have entered her head. Sharon, on the other hand, has several pieces of shot in her right leg. One was bleeding profusely, and he needed to take her to their mother. George said to Gloria, "Sharon is shot and I need to get her home fast. Be careful, stay off the path, and try to get back to the house. When you get there, hide in the garage until I come to get you."

Without someone to follow, Gloria couldn't see much farther than the end of her nose, and she got a bit lost as she wandered through the woods to return to the house. She wished she had been able to find her glasses after her brother Dick had thrown them into the bean field on the way home from the bus stop a few days earlier.

Dick had been angry with Gloria because she had refused to go with him into the bean field and "lie down." Dick hit her

in the face, and her glasses cut into her nose and then bled a lot. He took her glasses and laughed at her. "I guess you won't be going far without these." He threw them as far as he could into the field.

Gloria was at his mercy once the glasses were gone. Dick pushed her farther into the rows of beans and made her lie down in the dirt. He held her by her legs and pulled her underpants off, throwing them into the field too. He told her that she could look for them after he was done. He shoved her down to the ground and got on top of her, forcing her legs apart and holding her hands above her head to keep her from hitting him. What Dick did to her next hurt horrifically, and she bit him in her desperation to get him to stop. He struck her in the eye again, and her nose started bleeding again and now her eyebrow too. His weight pressing her hard into the ground made it difficult for her to breathe. She stopped biting and gave up.

Gloria spent hours afterward hunting for her glasses in the bean field, but it was getting dark and her sister Susie came looking for her. Susie told Gloria that Dick was complaining about her and later, they would talk about what she was doing wrong so Dick wouldn't get mad at her again.

When Gloria returned to the farmhouse after the walk with her father, she found that her mother had already left to take Sharon to the hospital. George was waiting for her on the front porch; he cleaned and put a bandage on her forehead, making sure there was no more blood or birdshot anywhere. George told Gloria that if their mother asked, she was to tell

the same story he had told their mom. "I told her that Dad had tripped and the shot gun went off accidentally. I told her that I had been nearby and heard the gunshot blast and Sharon crying." George said, "Look, Gloria, never go anywhere alone with our dad again. Never let Sharon or Susie go anywhere with him either. He wants to hurt you all and he is incredibly mean."

Gloria understood and agreed with George. When the shotgun went off, she realized exactly how crazy their father was. She was not stupid for a seven-year-old; she knew that their father had shot them intentionally. She had seen him raise the shotgun out of the corner of her eye. Neither she nor Sharon had ever even yelled "snake," only he had. She was very afraid that he might keep trying to kill them.

Later, Sharon came home with their mother, and Gloria was relieved to see she was still alive and, mostly, unhurt. She was crying. She would not allow anyone but George and her mother come near her. Gloria was able to tell her that she was sorry later, feeling that she should have really taken Sharon and ran instead of listening to their father.

The next day, a police car showed up at their house. The five kids all watched as they placed handcuffs on their father and put him in the back of the patrol car. Their father was acting very reasonably, telling the officers that it was an accident.

When Sylvia had taken Sharon to the emergency room with birdshot in her leg, the hospital had called the police. She told the doctors what George had told her, even though she

had her doubts. She was beginning to realize that Bud was one mean son of a bitch. Now as the patrol car pulled out of the driveway with their father inside, all of the kids breathed a collective sigh of relief. Maybe he would go to jail forever. There was always hope.

The day after he was taken away in handcuffs, their father was back, as if nothing had even happened. Except now, he was angrier than ever and somehow pleased with himself that he had gotten away with it. It seemed to Gloria there was no help; no one cared that they were in grave danger. *Someday*, she thought, *one of us will die because of him.* She decided then no one would help. She could count on no one but herself.

Everyone always believed what her father said; he was very good at convincing others that he was telling the truth. It seemed to her that he liked that part of the process as much as he liked the hurting part. Gloria had begun to realize that there were some distinct differences between her family and other families.

For one thing, they never had any pets that stayed around very long. So many small pets had disappeared that their mom quit letting them have any dogs or cats. One time, a puppy they had picked out at the grocery store had wound up hanging from its neck on the clothesline where their mom dried clothes. Gloria had never seen her mother cry before, and her father just stood there and smiled.

George was right; he was dangerous. Gloria thought that maybe her brother Dick was crazy bad too. Some of the awful

197

things Dick made the girls do had begun to seem like just normal, everyday things. George did not know about that stuff. Gloria was beginning to suspect that this was another difference between her family and others. She was never supposed to talk about it; if she did, her mother would die.

{ 28 }

Gloria Learns the Ropes

A week or two after the incident in the bean field with Dick, Susie came to find Gloria. Gloria had been reading, as usual; it was always hard to get her attention if she was reading.

Susie sat down on the couch next to Gloria and told her it was time for lessons. Gloria tried to ignore her sister since she did not understand what Susie was saying. It was summer and Gloria did not want to think about lessons since there was no school. She spent her days playing with her sisters or reading. She had chores to do but that would not be until later.

Susie took her book and laid it down on a table. "We are going right now. Read that later," she said to her sister. Gloria got up from the couch and followed her sister outside. The two girls crossed the side yard between the house and the fields. When they were close to the garage, Susie grabbed Gloria's hand and headed up the stairs to the rooms above the garage.

Gloria had never been inside the rooms up there before and pulled her hand back. Susie held tight to her hand and told her to come upstairs with her. Gloria said to Susie, "We are not

supposed to go upstairs; it is forbidden. I do not want to get into trouble."

Susie replied, "Don't worry; I have seen Uncle Richard and some black girls going up here. He is not here, though, so he will not know."

"Okay," Gloria replied, "Just don't touch anything."

As they climbed the stairs, Gloria was wary of the rooms; she did not know what to expect and it scared her. Susie was insistently tugging at Gloria's hand and telling her to hurry up. When they got to the top of the stairs, Susie opened the door and Gloria followed her inside. There was a lock on the inside of the door and Susie latched it. Gloria thought to herself, *that was weird*; she did not see any reason to lock themselves inside.

Why are we here? Gloria wondered. She looked around at the room that was vacant except for some lumber and a few tarps. When Gloria stepped into the next room, she saw only a tarp, crumpled up on the floor. "What kind of lesson is this?" Gloria asked her sister.

Susie looked at her sister and walked over near the tarp. "You remember I told you that Dick was mad at you because of the things you did in the bean field?"

Gloria nodded her head but kept quiet. "Well, Dick wants you to have some lessons so that you don't do that again."

Gloria shook her head no and said, "I don't care if he did not like it; I did not want him to do that. I do not want any lessons about Dick."

At that point, Susie lifted the tarp to reveal Dick lying under the tarp, completely unclothed. His penis was fully erect. When Gloria saw her brother, she turned and ran to the door, forgetting the lock. As she pulled on the door in her panic, her sister caught her and pulled her back into the other room. Dick was sitting up now and told Gloria that she needed some lessons so that it would not hurt so badly when he wanted to have sex with her.

Gloria stared her brother down and said, "That hurt because of you; not because of me." Gloria was mad and hurt that her sister had betrayed her. She looked at her brother and said, "You can always have sex with Susie; she knows what to do. Just leave me alone."

Dick replied, "Yes, I can have sex with Susie, but she is older than you and knows what to do already. You are younger, and I would really like to teach you what I like so you can have sex with me too."

Gloria felt trapped; she was unable to get away since she was too short to reach the lock on the inside of the door. There was no one else around; Uncle Richard was not there, and not that he would be helpful. Because the door was locked and despite her fears, she was going to have to do what Dick wanted. She was afraid of Dick; he was getting older and Susie was acting as if she knew all about sex. She realized she was afraid of Susie now too.

Gloria sat down on the floor and asked, "What if Uncle Richard shows up?"

Dick replied, "He was the one who told me I could use this place. He told me that he has sex all the time with the girls that work for him. He told me, for using it, Susie would have to have sex with him if he wanted it, but we will not tell him about you."

Susie took Gloria over to sit beside Dick and the lesson began.

Gloria watched as Susie did things to Dick that Gloria had never known was possible. She was not sure some of those things should be done. She watched as Susie put her mouth on Dick and rubbed his penis. She saw some white, sticky stuff come out of Dick and suddenly, she understood more. Gloria threw up all over the floor and herself.

Dick jumped up and yelled, "Gross! That is puke! You are going to have to clean it up!"

Gloria put one hand to her head and one to her stomach and whined, "I don't feel so good."

Dick told Gloria that the things Susie did was what he wanted her to do. Dick said that he would not put his cock inside her since it hurt too much. Gloria merely nodded and put her hand on her stomach and wretched. Dick jumped back and told Gloria, "You will do things to me or else I will hurt you bad." Gloria just nodded, feeling lucky that she had won a reprieve for now. The next time, she would not be that lucky.

As she walked back to the house, she thought it could be worse. It could be Uncle Richard, who always made her feel ugly. *On the other hand*, she thought, *it could be her father.*

However, she thought, *I think I know the limits of my father's craziness; I do not know how far Dick will go.*

{ 29 }

No Place to Hide

When Gloria was at home, she would often hide in the attics that opened off the girls' bedroom. She would grab a book and a blanket and settle in behind one of the trunks on the floor to read. She had done this many times without discovery, so she began to develop a feeling of safety and comfort in the attic. It was dusty but not bad. One day, her sister saw her go into the attic and followed her in. She told Gloria that they had to stay out of the closet; their mother had said so. Gloria did not care and told her sister to leave her alone.

Susie told their mom that she had found Gloria in the attic. The next time she saw her mother, she told her not to go into the attic anymore and leave the trunks in the attic alone; nothing there belonged to them. Gloria had never paid much attention to the trunks, but her mother's comment changed that.

The next day, Gloria snuck into the closet and opened a few of the trunks to see what was in them. Books, books, and more books; there were more books than Gloria had ever seen outside of a library. Gloria looked to see if she knew any of the titles but did not. She was a bit worried about being

caught, but this was so neat that she sat down and started reading. Soon, she had fallen asleep next to the trunk, holding a book in her hands.

Something woke Gloria up and she sat up, unclear about what was happening. She saw her brother Dick coming toward her; she had been caught. Dick said, "You are not supposed to be here, let's go. You are just where Susie said you would be." Before that could even sink in, Dick said, "I could tell Mom where I found you or . . . you could give me sex instead."

Gloria looked at Dick and boldly said, "Tell Mom, I don't care." Dick reached out and grabbed her by the hair; he told her to get her blanket and put it on the floor near the attic door. It hurt when he pulled her hair, using it to control her movements. Dick forced Gloria onto the blanket and took her panties off.

He opened his pants and took out his penis and then knelt down and tried to force himself inside of Gloria. "Damn it!" Dick said. He was unable to push himself inside of Gloria. He sat back and said to her, "Spread your legs farther apart." She laid there not moving, and he forced her legs open himself. He tried again without success. His penis was starting to go limp and he rubbed himself. He leaned over Gloria and put his mouth between her legs to get her wet. Gloria just lay there, acting as if nothing was happening. "Don't you like this?" Dick asked Gloria. Gloria did not reply, just kept staring at him.

Gloria was very small for eight; she was smaller than most third graders and was smaller than most of the kids in the first grade at her school. She knew that whenever some man wanted to have sex with her, she was too small for them to put their penis inside of her. Gloria would just lie there, impassive, until they gave up and went away. She did not have anyone she could tell; even her sister was helping them now.

However, when Dick put his mouth on her, Gloria cringed in revulsion. She did not want him to touch her and he had just gone too far. Gloria took her leg and tried to kick her brother, but he was faster. "No, I do not like that; you are disgusting," Gloria fired at her brother and tried to kick him again.

Dick grabbed both her ankles and held them together with one hand. Gloria told him to let her go saying, "You can't do anything with me if you don't fit."

Dick looked at her, still holding her ankles and said, "No, but you can watch this." Dick began to masturbate and did not let go of Gloria's ankles until he came all over himself. Knowing that he could not chase her with that all over his clothes, she jumped up and ran from the attic. She wished there was a lock on the outside of that door.

{ 30 }

The Report

There were neighbors living just down the road, between her house and the bean field. They had a little girl about Gloria's age named Laura. Laura and Gloria would walk home from the bus stop together. Sometimes, they would play together if there was time. They would explore the woods around their homes and build forts from Spanish moss. Gloria was not sure that she liked the mother; there was an older sister as well. The two women were so big that the whole house shook when they walked across the floor.

Susie was always busy with something else and she was keeping secrets. Gloria was still mad at her about the lessons. Gloria felt that her sister had betrayed her so that she would not have to have sex with Dick as much.

One day, Gloria was sitting outside and the little girl next door walked up. She told Gloria that her mom wanted to know if she would like to go swimming at the lake with them. Gloria agreed to go and ran into the house to get her swimsuit. She told her brother George where she was going. George, busy with his homework, just waved her away, and Gloria ran out the back door to leave with her friend.

The girls ran next door and hopped into the car that was taking them to the lake. There were the two women and three young girls on their way to the lake. The two women were Laura's mother and big sister. Gloria had not seen them get into the big car, but both women took up the entire front seat. From where they sat, they touched the car doors and their sides touched in the middle of the seat. Gloria was amazed; she had never seen any two people that big. She wondered how they got in and out of the car.

When they reached the lake, the three girls slid out of the back seat and ran to the lake. It was not long before Gloria noticed a man picking up kids and tossing them into the lake. The kids seemed to be having fun, and Gloria was unused to any man being that nice to kids, unless he wanted something.

Gloria watched for a while; each of the kids that the man picked up and tossed laughed and came back again. Gloria looked at the man and realized that he was as big as her father was and must be just as strong. She saw one of her friends from school be picked up and tossed into the water; Gloria laughed with her, but kept her distance from the man. Her friend from class, Cindy, had long, curly auburn hair. Gloria thought that Cindy had the prettiest hair she had ever seen before.

Cindy came over to her and said, "Hi."

Gloria replied, "Hi that looks like fun." Cindy asked Gloria if she wanted to have a turn. Gloria's eyes got wide with fear, and she said that she was not able to.

Cindy looked at Gloria and told her, "No, really, it is okay; that is my Daddy and he is really nice." Gloria decided to try it but was too shy to go over to the man and ask for a turn, so Cindy took her over. Cindy introduced Gloria to her father and her father asked Gloria if she would like a turn. He laughed and asked Cindy if she thought it would be okay with Gloria's parents. Gloria told Cindy's daddy that her parents were not there.

"Okay, so up you go!" was his reply. He picked Gloria up and supported her with one hand on her back and another between her legs. He immediately tossed her right into the water. *This is fun*, Gloria thought; she got right up and joined the line to go again. Cindy's daddy kept going for what seemed like hours. Gloria noticed that he held all of the girls and boys the same way before he tossed them. It did not feel funny to Gloria like when her father, Dick, or Uncle Richard touched her between her legs. Gloria decided that it was okay, and just relaxed and kept having fun.

After a while, her friend Laura that she had come with told her that her mother wanted to talk to her. Gloria went to the car and got into the back seat. Gloria had not noticed that neither of the big women had even been out of the car.

Laura's mother asked her if she noticed that the man who was throwing her into the water was playing with her pee-pee. Gloria looked at the woman, confused about why she was asking about that. The woman looked at her and restated her question, "Gloria, did you know that the man who was tossing you into the water was molesting you?" Gloria could not be-

lieve what she heard; she told the women in the car that he was doing the same thing to every kid he tossed into the water.

The women then started peppering her with questions. "Did he put his fingers inside you bathing suit?" "Did he rub you between your legs when he was holding you?"

Gloria told them once again that, "No, nothing dirty was happening." She told them that he was Cindy's daddy and a very nice man. The women began to try convincing Gloria that what he was doing was "evil" and "the devil's work" and that it was "just plain dirty and wrong for a man to touch little boys and girls between their legs." With that, Laura's sister got out of the car, went to the pay phone, and called the police.

When the police arrived, they asked Gloria to point out the man that had molested her. Gloria told the police that he was nice, not mean and that he had done the same thing to all of the kids that were playing there. The two big police officers sat beside Gloria in the back seat of that car and questioned her for what seem like a long time. When they got out of the car, they went over to Cindy's daddy and took him to the patrol car. They told everyone else to leave the lake until tomorrow. They took Cindy's daddy to jail.

When they got home, Laura's mother talked to Gloria's mom, who was getting ready for work. When Sylvia heard what had happened and Laura's mother was gone, she asked Gloria if she was okay. Gloria told her mother yes, nothing had happened and that Laura's mother and sister had made her

tell the police that Cindy's daddy had hurt her. "But he didn't, Mommy, I swear."

Sylvia looked at Gloria and said, "I am glad you were not hurt, but I don't want you over at Laura's house again. You are never to tell the police anything but the truth; Laura's mother is an evil-minded, bad person who created serious trouble and used you to do it. She is not nice and would hurt you too if she wanted to."

Gloria looked puzzled; because her mother had never hurt her, she did not think that women would do that. Then she remembered Aunt Pete and her own sister and realized her mother was right.

Gloria felt bad; she worried for weeks about what she had done. She knew what men who bothered little kids were like and Cindy's daddy had not made her feel like that at all.

{31}

The Big Fight

As 1962 became 1963, not much had changed at the Peterson house. Sylvia worked nights; there was no choice. Bud continued waiting until Sylvia left for work before heading home, drunk and mean, as usual.

If it was possible, Bud was becoming meaner than ever. He was bored from not working and resented Sylvia for dragging him to Florida, leaving his family and friends behind. When he brought this up, Sylvia would tell him to feel free to hit the road.

He was frustrated as well; his every attempt at eliminating one or two of those children had been unsuccessful. Somehow, each attempt ended with little to no physical damage to any of the kids. He had decided it was Sylvia and George's fault. For some reason, George always seemed to show up at the wrong moment. Bud decided that he needed to be more clever about his plans.

To vent some of his frustration, he would often join the children at the dinner table in the evening. Sylvia would prepare dinner, having the girls set the table just before she left for work. Bud was supposed to clear the table and clean the

dishes after dinner. Bud always made the girls do the dishes, however, calling it women's work. From the time she could stand on a chair and reach the sink, Gloria had to do dishes whenever her mother was at work.

On those nights, when Bud would sit at the dinner table with the kids, he would pick at anything they did; he called it "bad manners." Bud sat at one end of the table, he would make the girls sit one on each side, and Sharon was in the high chair. The two boys sat next to each of the girls. Bud wanted all of them within easy reach.

When the kids were eating dinner, if Bud thought they were eating too slowly, he would take the food from their plates and put it on his own, saying, "Well, if you don't want it, I will eat it." Other times, he would watch, and if one of the kids put their hand or elbow on the table, Bud would reach out and stab them in the hand with his fork.

Having someone stab a fork into your hand hurts badly. Gloria and her siblings took to eating one bite at a time, keeping their hands in their laps in between each bite. This gave Bud more opportunity to take their food away for being too slow, but it was much less painful.

One evening, as Bud sat in his chair drinking, waiting for one of the kids to give him an excuse, Sharon came over to his side. The three-year-old put out her arms, asking to be held, but Bud was in no mood to put up with her. He sat there, shook his head, and said no, but Sharon began to cry and stand there. Bud thought to himself, *the other kids know better than to bother me; maybe this one needs some training.*

He looked around for one of the other kids to get her, so he would not have to put up with the whining and crying. She was really getting on his nerves. The other kids were all upstairs doing their homework or hiding. Sharon wasn't allowed to walk up the stairs alone; she had to be carried, lest she fall.

Bud suddenly realized that letting her go up the stairs was a great idea. Bud took her by the hand, and pulling hard on her arm, led her to the stairway. He set Sharon upon the first floor landing. Whispering in her ear, he told her to go upstairs, that her brother George was up there waiting for her. Sharon put her palms down on the first step and started to crawl up the stairs. Bud stopped her and, lifting her hands, took her back to the landing. He told her that she had to walk up, not crawl.

Sharon was a small girl, petite like her mother, and started up the stairway with difficulty, nearly losing her balance with each step. Hanging onto the banister, she was able to make her way up the first two steps, unsteadily. Bud told her not to hold onto the banister, that she needed to learn how to walk up the stairs by herself.

George, who had been on the top landing where his sisters' beds were set-up, heard the last exchange. He stood up and quietly walked to the banister and peeked over. He could see his father at the bottom of the stairs watching Sharon's wobbly steps as she tried to climb the steps. Then Bud stepped back, out of sight, to watch.

George immediately walked down to the bottom of the stairs and picked up Sharon before she could fall. He turned to

carry Sharon up the steps with him into the girls' room so that he could finish helping them with homework. As he turned, Bud commented to George, "You do that just like a mommy; would you like to be a mommy some day?"

George replied, "It would be better than being like you."

Bud started yelling at George to get his ass down the stairs, calling him names and throwing things about in his fury. George turned and came back down the stairs to face his father.

George was angry about what had just happened and at fifteen years old, he was beginning to form his own opinions and make judgments about his parents. He sat Sharon on the floor, far from the stairs, and then turned to face his father who was still in a fit of fury.

Bud came toward George, and without warning, punched him in the face. George, who was not as large as his father, did not go down as Bud expected him to. George put all of his weight behind a punch that caught Bud off guard.

Bud was infuriated; he never believed that one of his own kids would come after him. He began pummeling George with his fists, and George continued to respond with the same anger. When the fighting began to get close to Sharon, George told his father, "Let's take this outside." Turning on his heel, George headed for the door. Bud followed George outside and they continued to punch each other.

Whether Bud had the advantage because of his size or because he was so inebriated that he could not feel pain, George began to falter. He tried to walk away; he put his hands up and

said, "Enough, stop, you win." Bud was still enraged and kept coming at George anyway. George turned and ran into the fields, his father following him.

Bud was determined that George was going to get the beating he deserved for not minding his own business. He ran after him into Richard's fields and continued to punch and kick George all over his body. When George was down, Bud continued to kick him as he lay on the ground for several minutes longer. Then, with one last kick, he said to George, "Don't you ever fucking speak to me like that again; you are a pussy spy for your bitch mother. If I could, I would kill you both."

George lay there for some minutes, catching his breath and assessing the pain to see how bad it was. After ten minutes or so, he got to his feet and found that he was able to move with some pain. It was not the worst pain he had ever experienced, but that was the worst beating ever dealt to him by his father.

George avoided his mother the next day so that she would not see the bruises and scrapes on his face. Uncle Richard confronted him about the damage done in the field. Uncle Richard asked him what had happened. George told him that he and his father had been in an argument, and he had run into the fields to get away from him. Uncle Richard said, "It looks like you had a fight right there in the field."

George nodded and told him, "Yes, he followed me and kept beating me out here."

The next day, Uncle Richard spoke to Bud about the fight and the damage. He told Bud that because he caused the dam-

age, he would have to pay for it or work it off in the fields. Bud asked him how much damage they had caused. Richard told him, "About $400 or so; I would rather you pay me in cash instead of working it off."

Later, Aunt Rose called the house and told Sylvia that she needed to look for another place to live. Richard, she said, would not put up with the damage that Bud was creating because he could not handle himself around the kids. Sylvia agreed that she would find another place as soon as possible. "I am so sorry, Rose; he certainly hasn't changed for the better since we arrived here," she said.

One day, before they left this home and moved again, Gloria came home to find her mother upset and crying. "What is wrong, Mommy?" Her mother told her that her father had passed away and that she was sad. "Grandpa, died?"

"Yes," her mother said, "I will have to be gone for a week, so be good for you father, alright?"

Gloria, with tears on her face, said, "I will try, Mommy, please tell Grandpa that I miss him." Her mother cried and said she missed him too."

While her mother was gone for the next week, everyone was very subdued. The kids were just beginning to feel the implications of leaving Indiana. They would never see their grandpa again, the only grandpa that Gloria had ever known. They had left every aunt, uncle, and cousin behind. Every grandparent was only a fond memory. They also had left every opportunity for rescue from this madness.

{32}

Old Orlando Highway

When Sylvia returned to Florida after attending her father's funeral, she immediately began looking for a new home. Rose and Richard had given them notice, and she did not want to take advantage of their love and support.

She found a house that was in the same school district so the kids would even stay in the same schools. The house was not great, but it was big enough and was close to her job at Spencer's Steakhouse.

The house was several miles west of Sanford Avenue at a sharp bend in the road. The house itself was nothing to speak of, just three bedrooms, a kitchen, living room, and the requisite screened porch. *It will do just fine*, she told herself, and she could afford it since Bud had not worked since they arrived in Sanford.

There was a silage plant near the house and in the summer, it smelled terrible. A small creek ran past the house in the back, loaded with snakes. On the sharp bend in the road, just past the house, there were many accidents. People tended to

drive too fast along the road and were surprised when they came upon the bend too quickly.

There was an expensive two-story home across the road from the house. Compared to that single polished gem, the other homes around had long ago lost any shine they might have had. Most of the roads along the Old Orlando Highway were dirt roads. Some of the homeowners had that peculiarly southern habit of saving every car or truck they ever owned in their yard.

The kids would gather where the dirt roads met with the highway to catch the bus to school. In the afternoon, they got off the bus in the same place. It was there, at the bus stops, that Susie and Gloria made friends. It was a way for the girls to have an opportunity to escape their homes, even if it was infrequent. The girls were not allowed to bring friends to play at their house. Both of the girls were too afraid of what might happen if they brought home any friends.

{ 33 }

The Sunday Drive

Bud walked into the kitchen looking for trouble. He was bored, and with Sylvia home all day on Sundays it seemed impossible to find a way to satisfy his need. He felt as though he could literally feel the nerves dancing under his skin. She really was no fun anymore; all she did was complain about everything he did, or as she put it, "everything he didn't do." He was sick and tired of listening to the bitch piss and moan, and if he had to stay here and listen to it all day and night, well let's just say there might be some real hell to pay. He was just itching to hit her.

However, Bud knew well that if he hit Sylvia, that was going to be the end of his meal ticket. After all, she did work nights and that did two things: it paid for the booze and it kept her out of the way most nights so the fun could begin.

Instead, as he walked through the kitchen of the little house on the Old Orlando Highway, he said to Sylvia, "I am going to take the girls and go get some beer and go for a drive."

Sylvia replied, "Just leave the girls here and go for your drive; I don't have any money to give you for beer. Would

you pick me up some hamburger at the store on your way back? I need it for supper."

Bud said, "Sure, by the way, did that lady ever pay you for that pup of Friskie's she bought?" Sylvia told him that the woman was to pay her in two weeks and that the money would help pay the rent.

The family had moved to the house a few months back when Sylvia's Aunt Rose had tired of all the trouble caused by Bud when they had rented the house she owned at their farm. It had been a huge house with plenty of space for the family and nice and affordable rent. Aunt Rose and Uncle Richard had asked them to move out after one of Bud's beatings had sent George running into the mustard fields to evade him, and the ensuing chase had resulted in many hundreds of dollars in damages. Rose Ransbottom could not abide her niece's husband and had done her best to help, but there were limits to even her patience.

Sylvia felt claustrophobic in this small and dirty old house. She was angry that, once again, she had to change the kids' lives because Bud could not control himself. As always, the kids were quiet as mice about what had happened. She was sure something had happened. She was looking out the window and thinking, washing dishes, and saw Bud put both girls into the back seat of the car. She dried her hands on a kitchen towel and headed for the door, but by the time she got there, all she saw was the back end of the car driving away. *Dammit*, she thought, *he has no business with those girls in the car; he is probably going to be drinking.* Worried, she went back to

her housework. She still had washing and dinner to go once she finished cleaning the dishes.

Bud came up behind the two girls and shouted, "GET IN THE CAR!" Both Susie and Gloria jumped at the sound of their father's voice. They had been engrossed in a conversation about school and had not heard him approach. Bud laughed when the girls jumped; they scampered back from him and he raised his fist and shook it at them. "I told you to get in the car, now hurry!" Bud said through clenched teeth; he did not want to yell again. He needed to get the girls in the car without that bitch finding out before he could get out of there. It was time for a little fright time to keep them in line.

Both of the girls jumped into the back door he had opened, looking at the house to see if their mom was watching and would save them. They whispered to each other and Bud said, "Shut up. Your mother told me to take you with me."

Susan grabbed Gloria by the hand and Gloria stared at her wide-eyed; the girls spoke without words, using gestures and their eyes. Shrugged shoulders meant, "what"; a shake of the head meant, "I don't know" pursed lips meant, "be quiet." Messages flashed back and forth between the girls. Then Susie whispered, "I am scared, too." The girls sat closely together on the back seat of the car, holding hands. Their father drove on not saying much. That was never a good sign. The two girls were silent. It was not safe to cry.

Finally, after a long time, their father spoke. "We are going for a Sunday drive. You girls remember the pups that Friskie had a while back? One of the women that your mom works

with bought one of the puppies and we are going to go visit the puppy. Would you like to do that?" Neither girl answered; they never knew what to say to him. When he was nice, it was even more frightening. The girls looked at each other with eyes wide and shrugged their shoulders. Bud looked back in the rearview mirror and asked, "Well?" Finally, the girls both said, "OK." Bud laughed, "Good, this is going to be fun." The girls looked and each other and Gloria began to cry; Susie looked and pursed her lips, if one of them got it, they both would. Gloria stopped crying; she knew her father's laugh too well.

After a while, the three arrived at house trailer sitting on a small property. Not far off the road, the property was well shaded and sat close to a creek. Many trees shaded it; some of them were gardenias, and elephant ears were growing in the flowerbeds, and the grass was trimmed and deep green.

The girls both thought that anyone who took good care of their house like this probably took good care of the puppy too. Their father knocked on the door to the trailer, and after a few minutes, no one had answered, so their father had the girls get out of the car. He knocked once again and soon a woman answered the door.

Their father told the woman that he was Sylvia's husband and that the girls had been asking if they could come and visit the puppy she had bought. She hesitated for a moment, then went inside and came back out with the puppy, giving it to Susie. The girls began to pet the puppy and play with it on the

grass, and as they moved away a bit, their father and the woman moved with them.

Suddenly, Bud scooped up the puppy from where the girls played with it on the grass. Bud explained that he had come to collect the payment for the pup. The woman explained to Bud that she had already told Sylvia that she wasn't going to be able to pay for the puppy for another two weeks. Bud told her that wasn't good enough and that he would just have to take the puppy back. Bud told the girls to get back into the car and the girls did just that.

From the back seat, the girls watched as their father held onto the puppy by the neck. He threatened to wring its neck unless the woman gave him the money he wanted. The girls could hear the woman beg and cry for the puppy's life as he continued to make threats. They quit watching and covered their ears as they saw their father twist the puppy's neck and throw it on the ground. He grabbed the woman by the neck as she began to scream. He told her to shut the fuck up; then he pushed the sobbing woman back inside her trailer. He followed her in; the girls could hear the woman scream and cry, and then her father yelled something and the woman was silent.

A short time later, their father returned to the car and both girls sat still and looked straight ahead, afraid to say or do anything. Their father started the car and began to drive; both girls, too shocked to move, sat, and held onto each other.

After a time, their father began to talk, not to them, but aloud about what had happened. He was feeling the rush of

what he had done and just could not contain it; he needed to feel it all over. He began to laugh hysterically and mock the woman. "Oh, please don't hurt my puppy!" and "Oh, no please don't hurt me!" "Please! No!" he mocked her in a derisive, female tone. Too stunned and too scared to talk, the two girls laughed along, because to do otherwise was to ensure a fate the same as the one met by that woman and her puppy. The girls watched their father carefully for any sudden moves, laughing all the while with tears running down their faces, hands tightly holding on to one another. The girls' father continued his hysterical behavior all the way home; he was sure that these girls would never tell, after all they knew what would happen if they did.

{ 34 }

Cottonmouth Rescue

Time seemed to slow to a crawl the year that they lived in the house on Old Orlando Highway. George and Dick were in high school in town. While George focused on his studies, Dick graduated from delinquency to misdemeanor crimes. Both of the boys had responsibilities at home. Dick avoided coming home, so George often took care of his three sisters on his own. Sometimes Dick would bring home friends, and George required that they remain outside. George was clearly in charge; even if Dick resented it, he did not want to change it and have to help with the girls.

Most nights, their father did not come home until it was very late and the kids were asleep. After the ruckus when they lived in Uncle Richard's farmhouse, he was leery of George and how much control he had over the kids. He would go to a bar where he could sit and drink without having to watch the kids. Sometimes, though, Bud would surprise them and begin an impromptu training session. This usually ended with one or more of the kids making too much noise. Therefore, Bud toned down his usual terror in order to avoid detection.

Gloria liked to be outside; it was nice and she wanted to wander the nearby woods. She often wandered about, looking at whatever creatures she found. The most poisonous one she ever found was a coral snake. It was in the fronds of a palmetto she was trying to climb. When her foot kicked loose the frond, it fell and exposed her to the coral snake. She swung quickly to the other side and ran like the wind, a lucky escape for sure. Another day, she found a copperhead moving slowly among the trees and stopped to watch. There was some excitement in being that close to danger. Gloria really did not care; she had been feeling that she would be better off dead anyway.

Recently, George had noticed that Gloria was complaining of chest pain. Concerned that there might be something wrong with her heart, George kept an eye on her realizing that it was probably just panic. One day, Gloria held her breath and locked her knees in panic then fainted, falling on the cement porch and hitting her head hard. When George explained to Gloria how it happened and what a panic attack was, Gloria understood. She decided that she should try harder not to let her fear get the best of her any longer.

Then, one day, Dick brought home a new friend; the boy seemed younger than Dick, but the rest of the Peterson kids just ignored him. That day, however, Gloria had found a bamboo cane-fishing pole and was messing around near the creek behind the house. Dick and his friend wandered up behind her, both of them carrying fishing rods, the real kind, not like Gloria's cheap cane pole. Dick said something to his friend

and began to walk up the creek to where the trees began. His friend stayed where Gloria was. Gloria would normally make a fast retreat whenever her brother showed up; today he had a friend and she felt safe staying where she was. The friend kept trying to engage Gloria in conversation and Gloria kept ignoring him. He was standing next to her, fishing in the creek. When Gloria would pick up her fishing pole and move it somewhere else, he would follow her.

Gloria was beginning to wonder what he wanted. Suddenly, he slapped his fishing pole on the creek bank where she was fishing. When Gloria asked him, "What did you do that for?" he told her that he had saved her from a cottonmouth moccasin that was about to bite her. Gloria looked around and seeing no snake, she just said, "Thank you."

Immediately, the boy said to her, "Don't you think you owe me something for saving your life?"

Gloria looked at the boy. "I told you thank you, which is all I have to give you."

Then the boy said to Gloria, "Your brother told me that you would give me sex."

Gloria turned to walk away and retreat to the safety of the house where her oldest brother was studying. As she turned, she ran right into Dick, who told her to do something nice for his friend. Gloria shook her head and tried to pull away from Dick. Only, Dick had a hold of her good and she could not break free. "Go ahead;" Dick told his friend, "I will hold her down while you fuck her." His friend stood there looking

doubtful and Dick said, "It is okay, she is used to it; you can even hit her and bite her if you want. She won't tell anyone."

"Okay," his friend said, "just help me get her down and pull her pants off."

Dick held Gloria down on the ground, pushing hard on her shoulders so she could not sit up. His friend put one knee between Gloria's legs and hit her once in the stomach. Dick yelled, "Bite her! Bite her!" His friend scooted down and bit Gloria hard on her thigh. Dick stopped him, telling him not to break her skin and then egged him on again.

As the boy pulled off Gloria's panties and tried to enter her, Dick said, "She is very small, so she might be too tight." The boy pushed his cock into Gloria and raped her. Gloria was crying and screaming loudly. The back porch screened door opened and George hollered out Gloria's name. At the sound of George's voice, both boys ran off into the woods and left. Gloria pulled on her panties and headed inside. She did not talk to anyone about what happened; there was no point.

As the year dragged on, there were the less frequent training sessions with their father, and it was just a matter of making sure that Dick had no opportunities to get her alone. Gloria was in the fourth grade, enjoying school immensely. Whenever a teacher or librarian questioned her about a bruise or cut, Gloria would just point out what a tomboy or klutz she was. No one ever doubted her.

{ 35 }

The Stepfather Next Door

Gloria had made a few friends and spent time at their homes. It was a respite for Gloria; she did not have to be constantly wary. One of the girls, Christie, would come over to her house sometimes. Several times, Gloria stayed the night at Christie's house. One Saturday, Gloria's mom said it would be okay and Gloria was elated. She had stayed there several times and was going to stay again that night. She packed her pajamas and toothbrush and was set to go. This was the only place she ever went without her sister Susie or one of her brothers. The girls got along very well and would spend time playing games or wandering around outside. This particular night, however, the girls had been playing indoors most of the evening and were getting ready for bed when they began jumping on the bed and laughing. It was nearly bedtime and Christie's stepfather opened the door and yelled at them to stop. "Cut that jumping out or I will come in there and beat you both."

The girls stopped jumping and were talking and giggling, as girls tend to do. Before too long, both girls forgot her stepfather's words and began jumping on the bed again. Once

again, he opened the door, yelling at them to stop and threatened them both. Neither girl seemed to notice that he was much more aggravated than the first time.

The girls settled down for a time. Not a bit sleepy, the girls began to talk and giggle again, trying to get to sleep. Suddenly, the stepfather burst through the door and yelled, "I warned you both to stop! Now I am going to beat you!" Gloria only half-believed him because he had already yelled twice. Her father never yelled once; he would just start hitting. Not expecting it, Gloria received a hard slap upside her head. He then started spanking and hitting Christie about her legs, arms, and head. When Christie was sobbing and promising never to jump on the bed again, he turned back to Gloria. He grabbed Gloria by her legs and tried to spank her. When Gloria kicked him away, he punched her arm. Gloria grabbed her arms and rolled up into a ball to protect her body; he began hitting her with his closed fist on her butt and her head. Gloria could not move fast enough to avoid his strikes, so she just lay still, curled up in that ball. His fists hurt badly, but she would not cry; crying only served to make her own father angrier.

The next morning, Gloria woke up early, before Christie, and got dressed. She grabbed her belongings, slipped out the back door, and headed home. She was sore everywhere, but could see no bruises; she would have Susie look later. Gloria wondered why people liked to hit her. What did she do that made people like her father, brother, and Christie's father so enraged that they wanted to take it out on her?

Monday morning, while waiting for the bus, Christie came over and apologized for her stepfather beating them. Gloria asked her if he did that all of the time and Christie replied, "Only when I don't obey." Christie asked Gloria if she was okay because he had hit her hard.

Gloria said, "That is okay, I have been hit much harder, I will be okay. However, I do not think I will stay at your house again. I like you, but that was too much." Christie nodded and the bus arrived just then; they both got on the bus and never spoke of it again.

Gloria's life returned to normal with only the occasional "session" as her father called it. Dick was usually out making trouble somewhere, but not always. However, there were still nights when the house turned into a pit from hell. The girls got the brunt of it, with Dick teaming up with their father and George trying to ignore it all.

{ 36 }

Gone For Good

Sylvia pulled her 1964 red Ford Falcon station wagon out of the driveway with her three young girls huddled on the back seat. She was amazed at the sudden clarity and determination she was feeling. There would be some difficult days ahead. For now, she needed to get her daughters over to her Aunt Rose's house. There, the four of them could finally have a night of peace. The girls were frightened, and as she turned in her seat and tried to reassure them, Sylvia saw the terror in their eyes.

Why should they trust her? It seemed that she had really let them down. Her suspicions had been building for some time that something was not right and apparently, things had been far worse than she suspected.

First, she must get to Rose's house and call the sheriff; forced to leave her two sons with her husband, he had threatened all of them if she had tried to leave. She needed to see to their safety soon. Then she would get the girls settled for the night. Not one of the girls uttered a sound; they all seemed frozen with fear.

Sylvia was just beginning to understand that all of those small pieces that never quite fit together made a much bigger picture than she ever suspected. Her neighbors had all asked to speak to her because they were concerned. Every night, they said, after she left for work, there were horrible noises that came from her home. Yells and screams, they told her, not just fighting but like someone was in terrible pain. They were afraid that some of the children were being hurt. They wanted her to do something to stop it. Immediately because, it was, they told her, more than they could bear to hear.

As Sylvia had confronted Bud with the neighbors' accusations, she asked him if he was hitting the children. Bud had replied, "Hitting? Hell, yes, I have been hitting them and worse. If you don't shut your fucking mouth, I will beat the shit out of you too!"

With that, Sylvia had walked to the house, stopping to tell her girls to get into the car on the way in. When they asked her why, she told them, "Don't ask questions, just do as I say," in a tone of voice that left no doubt as to what was expected.

Once she reached the house, she picked up her purse and looked for the two boys, telling them to go to the car. Bud came into the house and began to argue; "You are not taking the kids and leaving, I will beat the shit out of every one of you!" Bud placed himself between Sylvia and the boys; he would not let the boys leave. Sylvia looked outside and saw that the girls were waiting in the car, looking at the house with big, round, frightened stares.

George had seen the girls too and told his mother, "Go ahead, Mom, we will be okay." Dick nodded his head in agreement and told her to leave as well. Sylvia hesitated for a few moments and then acquiesced, knowing that it was better to get the girls out now without a big scene.

She turned to Bud and said, "I am going to call the sheriff to come and check out the claims that the neighbors made." She went out to the car with a threat of her own, "You lay one hand on these boys tonight, and I will be back to kill you myself."

Later at their Great Aunt Rose's house, the girls could hear their mother relating the details of the day to a sheriff's deputy and then later to an attorney and even a judge. Later that evening with Bud arrested, deputies brought the boys to Aunt Rose's house. Bud, forced to leave by court order, vacated the house two days later and Sylvia returned with the children.

Sylvia could not have known then that it would be decades before she knew any of the truth. She could not have known that she would die without knowing the entire truth of what happened. Children, who have been taught with pain and fear to hold on so tight to the shame and guilt, may never learn to let it go. They often believe that they are complicit in the crimes that have been committed upon them.

As the children and Sylvia begin to find out what a "normal" life felt like, Sylvia saw the children often huddling and whispering. She wondered what they were talking about, and sometimes there were fights, but that seemed normal. Things

seemed quieter and much nicer now, so Sylvia decided that it was probably best to let sleeping dogs lie.

Still, as the first year passed, she was having problems with Dick who seemed to have picked up his father's violent tendencies. Sylvia began to think back to when she and Bud were first married and when George and Dick were young. Even then, there were things that just did not seem right.

{ 37 }

Back Home Again

The kids were glad to get back to their own house. Aunt Rose was very nice to let them stay there, but it was not home. Sylvia was doubly glad, first to be home and to be past the ugliness of turning her husband out.

She decided that it would be best to get back to some semblance of normalcy as soon as possible. Sylvia went back to work and the kids went back to school. It was going to be hard; they would all have to do their share to take care of things. Sylvia had not felt so free in many years; she hoped that the kids felt the same. She knew that it had been bad for them; she was afraid there were things she did not want to know.

Knowing that it was going to be almost impossible for her to meet her financial burdens, she turned to Seminole County for help.

Seminole County, Florida had no programs to help, but they did offer to put her children up for adoption. Sylvia would not consider that offer. Knowing that her children had lived through some unknown hell, she could not imagine sending them to another.

When Sylvia returned to her job at Spencer's Steakhouse, her boss, Jim, asked to see her. Prepared to lose her job over her absence, she was surprised when he told her that he knew what had happened. He told her that, if she was willing, he would double her pay rate to $1.65 per hour (plus tips). He also told her that during the past few days, her husband, Bud, had shown up at the restaurant, demanding to see her. Jim Spencer told her that he had Bud arrested for trespassing, and he was ordered never to come on the premises again. Jim told her that she could work as many hours as she wanted; he also told her that she could work as a bartender. Sylvia was grateful; she thanked him and headed out to work.

Maybe, just maybe, Sylvia thought, *I will be able to make it.* For the first time in six years, she was beginning to have hope. She had almost lost hope when Bud followed them to Florida, but now she had the protection of the law. She was beginning to look forward to a new future.

About a month after Sylvia and the kids returned home, things were finally calming down. The kids had settled into the new routine, finishing their homework and dinner, and then settling down to read and get ready for bed. One night, Sylvia returned home from work; there she saw a dark figure waiting for her on the screened porch. As she opened the door with some trepidation, she could see that it was Bud waiting for her on the porch. Bud was very drunk; he had apparently been sleeping until he heard her car pull into the driveway. As she walked onto the porch, Sylvia asked Bud what he was doing there.

"I thought I would come to visit the kids and you," was his reply.

Sylvia looked at her soon to be ex-husband. "The judge told you not to come here and there would be no visitation until he made his divorce decree."

Bud began to yell at Sylvia, "Those kids are mine to do with as I please and no one, not even a judge, is going to tell me what I can or cannot do with my kids."

Sylvia looked at Bud and said, "Leave, or I will call the sheriff."

Bud looked at her and said, "First you have to get to the telephone." Sylvia put her keys in the door and unlocked it then she went inside. Before she could close the door and lock it behind her, Bud pressed in on the door trying to gain entrance.

George, awakened by the argument, had gotten out of bed to see what was going on. Bud, barred from the house by court order, was trying to force the door. As George walked into the living room, he could see his mother losing her battle to keep his father from forcing the door open. George quickly walked to the door and, throwing his weight into it, closed and locked the door on his father. He looked at his mother and told her to call the cops. Bud was enraged. "How dare you keep me out of my own house!" he shouted.

Sylvia was already on the telephone with the sheriff's office; the dispatcher assured her that there were deputies nearby and they would arrive in a few moments. As Sylvia walked out of the kitchen into the hallway, she could see that

all but the smallest of her children had been roused by the ruckus their father was making.

Sylvia assured her kids that everything would be all right and they should go wait in their rooms until the sheriff arrived. She knew her kids and knew they were not going to sleep again until they were sure that their father was gone.

True to the dispatcher's promise, shortly, two sheriff's cars pulled into the yard with lights and sirens going. The driver's door to both of the patrol cars sprung wide open and deputies exited. Both deputies pulled their side arms and ordered Bud to come out of the porch with his hands up. Bud complied, and one of the deputies checked his pockets and put him in the back seat of his patrol car. Sylvia could hear them tell Bud, "Sir, you are in violation of the court order issued in your case; you are under arrest."

Once Bud was in the car, the other deputy knocked on the front door and asked to come inside. Sylvia opened the door and let the deputy inside. He asked if the children were up and Sylvia told them, "All but one." The deputies asked Sylvia to bring her kids out to the living room; George got up and walked to the end of the hallway. "Come on out," he said.

One of the deputies asked the kids if their father had hurt them and they all nodded. The deputy asked, "Tonight?" The kids silently shook their heads. The deputy told Sylvia that she had a very well behaved bunch of kids. He told the kids that they were safe and they could go back to sleep. The kids filed back into the hallway, stood there, and listened as the deputy spoke to their mother.

He told her that his supervisor was aware of the situation. He said that the neighbors had been complaining for some time. Deputies, however, are unable to interfere in family business until a family member complained. He also told her that he had been one of the deputies that removed her husband from the house the day after she took the kids and left. The deputy told her, "Bud sat in my car and bragged about the things he had done to his own kids!" He told her that he had never heard such horrible things. "You should make sure he stays away and can't get near them again. Just call us anytime he gives you any trouble," the deputy said.

On his way out the door, he turned once again and told Sylvia, "The things he told me are part of my police report and that is filed with the court." Sylvia thanked them both, bid them goodnight, and locked the house up. She was glad that she had told the kids to lock the doors at night after they returned from school. She was not comfortable leaving them alone at night but had little choice.

{ 38 }

The Last Visit

Sylvia had taken her kids to Titusville to visit their father; he had called her and asked to see them. He had used the ruse of paying support and had asked Sylvia to bring the girls to the pier where he worked. Sylvia had coerced all three girls into her red Ford station wagon and driven over to the coast; she took George along for the long ride. When she arrived, Bud told her that he would give her the money at the end of the visit. She told him that she was not leaving Sharon with him because she was too small and could easily fall through the pier into the water and drown. She told the older girls, Susie and Gloria, to get out of the car and go with their father.

Bud had thought that Sylvia would get out of the car and stay during the visit. When Bud angrily grabbed for her arm and tried to force her from the car, she had driven off. She could feel his anger reflected in her rearview mirror.

After their mother left, Susie and Gloria followed their father out onto the pier to the store where he worked on the weekends. Gloria heard what her mother said that Sharon might fall through the pier and drown. As she walked out onto the pier, Gloria froze in fear, grabbing her big sister's hand.

247

She was terrified that she would fall through the cracks in between the boards in the pier and die. She was trying very hard not to cry and make her father even angrier.

Bud was angry; he had not planned on being stuck with these two brats all day. He took two cane fishing poles out from behind the counter and took the girls onto the pier behind the store. The store was a long narrow building that covered most of the width of the pier where it sat. There was room for a walkway in front; behind the building, there was only enough space left for an adult to move along the length of the building very cautiously. Bud walked the girls along the narrow space behind the building, laughing to himself at Gloria who had plastered herself against the wall of the building and clung to her sister's hand as though that would save her. He gave them the fishing poles, without hooks or bait, and told them to "pretend to fish." "If you catch anything," he laughed cruelly, "don't fucking bother me, I have to work!" The girls sat down carefully on the narrow ledge, fearful that they might slip and fall. No one would help them if they did, no one would see them. Their father told them to pretend to fish. Both girls sat on the ledge in the hot sun and held out their poles. Susie whispered to Gloria when she would become upset not to let their father hear because he might get angry and push them off. Gloria sat on the edge of the pier with a sharp pain in her chest from the effort it took for her to swallow her fear.

After several hours in the hot sun, both girls were hot and thirsty. They also needed to use the restroom. Susan, the old-

est sister, asked their father if they could have some water or
something to eat. He angrily told her, "I am not going to give
you food, things are not free! Go find a bathroom somewhere
else. *I told you NOT to fucking bother me!*" Susie took Gloria,
walking back toward where they had come from and found a
bathroom at the end of the pier. Both girls searched the parking lot frantically, looking for their mother's car to see if they
could get her to take them home. They looked for a time but
were afraid to leave the pier because they were afraid that
their father would get mad. They were not able to find their
mom's car from that distance, never mind the fact that Gloria
could not see much farther than the end of her nose. She had
lost her glasses when she was seven, and so far, there had
been no money to replace them. The girls found a spot of
shade and sat down for a little while. It was much nicer in the
shade; a light breeze cooled them by drying the sweat from
their small bodies. Very soon, it was time to go back so that
their father would not come looking for them; that would have
been very bad. The two girls again waited in the hot sun for a
very long time back on that narrow ledge, having completely
given up the pretense of fishing. Finally, their father came to
get them. He grabbed both of them up from the edge of the
pier by one arm and pulled them all the way back along the
pier to their mother's car. As the trio approached the car, the
girls could hear their mother say, "What the hell did you do?
Look at the sunburn on that child!"

George got out, settled the girls into the car, and asked
Gloria if her sunburn was hurting. "Just a little so far," she

responded. Sylvia knew that by bedtime Gloria would be in severe pain. Bud knew how easily she burned and had been completely irresponsible in his care of the girls.

She turned to Bud and asked, "Where is the support money?"

Bud laughed and said, "What money?" Then, he tried to grab her and pull her from the car to kiss her and she pulled away. She yelled at George to get in the car quick, before more trouble started. Bud took a swipe at her with his fist through the car window but barely connected as Sylvia drove away. Sylvia looked in the rearview mirror to see if he was running after them and breathed a deep breath of relief when she saw he was not.

Sylvia turned to children and told them, "I am sorry that you had to come here today; you don't have to come anymore. I promise." She told Gloria, "I am sorry that you have sunburn; we will put something on that when we get home."

Oddly, Gloria responded with, "That's okay, at least he didn't . . ." Then she trailed off, doing something with her hands that Sylvia did not quite catch. Susie grabbed her sister's hands to stop her.

{ 39 }

Dick Goes Rogue

One day, several months later, Gloria and Susie came home from school on the bus and found their mother at home. She normally left for work by the time the girls got home. The girls settled into their afternoon routine of a snack, homework, and chores. Gloria picked up the newspaper; it was her habit to read it daily. Since she usually completed her homework in class, she called reading the paper her "homework." If Susie was still not done with her own homework by the time Gloria was finished, she would read one of the dozen or so library books she always had checked out.

This day, when Gloria picked up the newspaper, the front page and one page behind that was full of holes. Someone had cut out several articles that had appeared in the newspaper that day. When Gloria asked her mom what had happened to the newspaper, Sylvia told her that she had cut out an ad that she wanted to use for shopping. Gloria asked if she could see the advertisement, because she liked to read the "whole" newspaper, not the "hole" newspaper. Sylvia told her no, that she had already been shopping and no longer had the ads. Her mother seemed more than just a little upset by her request. Gloria

sensed that her mother was not telling her the truth but had no idea why she would do that.

The next day, when she and Susie arrived at school, several kids surrounded them and asked the girls "why their brother had done that."

"What did he do?" Susie asked.

One of the kids told them, "Him and another kid stole a car from a teacher and then broke into his house, robbed it, and trashed it really bad."

Suddenly, the holes in the newspaper made sense to Gloria and she told her sister, "That is why Mom cut holes in the newspaper; she did not want us to read about it." The girls were upset but had to go to class.

Later at home, they asked their mother about what Dick had done; Sylvia looked at the girls and asked how they knew. Susie replied, "The kids at school told us and were making fun of us because of what he did."

Gloria was angry. "You should have told us, or let us read the paper. It hurt a lot to have those kids tell us instead of you." Sylvia sighed and thought it was hard to know exactly what to do sometimes. She got up and went into her room, returning with the articles she had clipped from the newspapers. The girls read the clippings and cried for a few minutes. They both knew that their brother hurt them, but they never thought he would hurt other people. They could not make any sense of it all.

Their mother told them, "I had the police take him to live with your father; I just can't be sure that he won't hurt some-

one else. I cannot leave him alone here with you guys while I have to work."

"Has he hurt either one of you girls?" she asked. The girls looked at each other and nodded slightly in response to their mother's question. "Well, he won't be back. The judge ordered him placed with your father until his court date," their mother replied. She never discussed it again.

Sylvia was becoming very worried about just how Bud and Dick had hurt the girls. She wished the girls would tell her so that she could help them, but they refused. The only way that Sylvia knew how to save her kids was to make the most positive life for them she knew how. She did not know how to talk to her girls about sex; her own mother had never broached the subject with her. She suspected that the two older girls already knew more about sex than she did, but she could not bear to think about it. Her guilt was great, but her burden was greater, so she set aside her guilt and got to work.

{ 40 }

Hog-Tied

Each day, after school, Gloria came home to an empty house. She was in the fourth grade and her mom thought that she would be "just fine" for the few hours until George and Susie arrived home from school. George was a senior at Seminole High School, and Susie went to Sanford Junior High School. Dick now lived with their father, Bud. Her mother was at work for the night.

Gloria enjoyed the few hours alone; it made her feel grown up and trusted. She spent the time reading or playing outside with the neighbor Pam. Today Pam was not home, so Gloria went inside and put her books down on the table in the kitchen. She picked up a book and started down the hallway to the bedroom that she shared with Susie and Sharon, her younger sister. At four, Sharon stayed at Shucksie's house while her mom was working.

As soon as Gloria left the kitchen and headed down the hallway, she realized that she was not alone in the house. When she heard movement in the front room, she called out "Hello?" then remembered that no one else should be there.

Before she could run out of the door, she heard a voice call out to her. "Hi, Magpie, what are you doing?" It was Dick, her older brother, who lived some 100 miles away. Gloria tensed

as she asked him why he was there. He replied, "I just came for a visit; aren't you glad to see me?"

"Does Mom know you are here?" Gloria asked her brother. "I am going to tell her when she gets here."

Dick replied, "When will she be home?"

"Not soon enough" was Gloria's curt reply, "can't you wait outside?" It made Gloria uneasy to be alone with Dick, and something about him being there was making the back of her neck tingle funny. Whenever Dick was back around, things happened and Gloria was just getting used to things being quiet. Her life had never been so nice before.

Since her father left, things were better; every night was quiet and she could read and do her homework. Gloria had glasses now and could actually see the blackboard at school, so her grades were getting very good. Her mom was so proud of Gloria because she had all A's on her last report card, and her big brother George was proud too. Mom had even made a cake to celebrate; that was a good time for them all.

Some months ago, when Mom had taken the girls and left, the sheriff had returned and made their father get his stuff and leave the house. Mom didn't make a lot of money; she worked as a waitress at Spencer's Steakhouse, and her boss helped her out by doubling her pay and having her tend bar so she could get better tips. Still, things were tough and money was tight, but Gloria had never been so happy. Dick had caused the only real trouble when he got in trouble with the law. He now lived with their father and things had been nice since then. Here he

was to spoil things again, and Gloria was not happy to see him. She was especially unhappy to be alone with him.

Dick was getting angry with his sister, who seemed unhappy to see him and reluctant to give him any information that was helpful. He had hitched all the way to Sanford from the coast and waited all day for one of the girls to show up. "Why don't you come over here and sit on the couch so we can catch up?" Dick said. Gloria resisted and Dick added, "Come on, I didn't come all this way to hurt you." Although every one of her senses was telling her to run, Gloria moved to the couch and sat down. The training to do as she had been told was a powerful thing. Still, Gloria felt that if she just did as she was told, she might escape unharmed.

Once she sat next to him, Dick began to ask her questions, and they were prying questions. "What time will Susie be home?" "What time will George be home?" "I sure would like to see them before I have to head back." "How do you like school this year?" "Have you met any boys you like?" "Do you let them touch you?" "Like this?" Dick placed is hand on her leg between her thighs and began to move it upward.

At the last question, Gloria was up and trying to run out of the room, but Dick had her by the arm. As she tried to escape, he threw her to the floor and slapped her hard across the face. Blood began to obscure her vision as the nosepiece of her glasses cut the tender skin below her left eye. Gloria cried out in pain as much as in fear, because although she thought she knew what came next, something seemed different this time.

She was scared because all of the blood and terrified that she could not see at all in order to get away from him.

Dick had previously coaxed and manipulated Gloria and her sister Susie into allowing him to touch them. He had never been violent before, always conciliatory in a manipulative way.

Dick turned Gloria onto her stomach, and she cried out again as he tied her feet and hands together behind her back. He had come prepared for a fight and brought some cord with him that he had found in the back of their father's car. He had some electrical tape and a knife, too, but was not sure why he would need them. He turned her over and took her glasses off her face. She was crying and she tried to bite his hand as he grabbed for her glasses. He cleaned the blood from her eyes and her glasses. Then he placed the glasses back on her face and said, "You are a stupid little bitch just like the rest of them, and you can just watch what I am going to do and learn to like it."

With that, Dick tore off her underwear and unbuttoned her dress. As the shocked nine-year-old lay there, Dick began to perform cunnilingus on her. Almost immediately, he began to rant, "Don't you bathe, you are a filthy little cunt, you should be beaten for not cleaning yourself."

Unsure of what he was doing or why he was so upset, Gloria felt so ashamed and began to plead, "Leave me alone, if you don't like me, please leave me alone."

"No!" Dick raged on, "You have always been too tight, I can never get my dick in your lousy little cunt! I am going to

fix that if I have to cut it open." Dick bit Gloria a few times on her stomach and legs. He thought about the knife he carried in his pocket but changed his mind. He rolled her over and tried to enter her from behind but could not; he had tied her legs and arms in his way. The rug muffled Gloria's cries. He hit her hard on the back a few times with his fists and told her to "shut up" or she would "eat his dick."

Suddenly, Dick left the room for the kitchen to get something to fix Gloria's lousy little cunt with. Dick was gone for what seemed like a very long time. She tried to wriggle loose of the knots that held her feet and wrists. However, Dick returned before she could make any progress; the cord was very tight.

When he returned, he had some kind of stick in one hand and his erect penis in the other. At the sight of her brother, Gloria began to scream at the top of her lungs, "I will tell if you touch me again. I will tell everybody in the world if you touch me again!" she screamed. Repeatedly she threatened to tell, yelling at the top of her lungs. Her yelling stopped him in his tracks for a few moments, unsure what to do next. Then Dick spun around in his tracks and left the room. Once again, he was gone for a bit. Gloria fought against her restraints, desperate but unable to free herself.

When Dick returned, he turned Gloria over onto her back again. He had a jar filled with a clear, colored liquid that he poured all over Gloria without saying a word. In his other hand, he held a box of matches. Now panicked, Gloria began

to scream uncontrollably, fearing that Dick would set her on fire and just leave her there to burn.

Dick held up a match and yelled at her, "If you ever tell anyone, I will burn you to death. I just poured gas on you and if you don't stop screaming, I will burn you right now!" He struck the match and nothing happened, no fire, no explosion. Dick laughed and said, "Next time, it will be real gasoline, not just piss."

Gloria began to cry and beg her brother to leave her alone. "Are you kidding?" was his only reply. She lay there quiet while he tried to thrust the stick inside her. He began complaining and returned to the kitchen to get something to "make it slicker."

He eventually returned to the front room, rubbing something on his penis then finished the job the only way he could by masturbating on her while calling her a "filthy cunt."

The only thing Gloria could think was, *why does this keep happening?* She felt herself floating away from what was happening to her as she lay there listening to her brother calling her names and hitting her while he masturbated.

Every time she began to feel safe, her father or her brother returned to wreak havoc in her life. She kept hoping that someday they would just kill her; she was too ashamed and too weak to do it herself. Shame was the only thing she could feel anymore, no love, no happiness, just shame. Even the pain of what they did to her had become nothing more than shame.

Gloria awoke on the floor in the front room to the sound of the school bus stopping down the road. She ached all over. She sat up, and as she became alert, she understood that she was no longer tied; her hands and feet were freed. She quickly stood, grabbed her clothing, and ran into the bathroom.

Confused, ashamed, and not wanting to talk about what had happened, she cleaned up her face and went to her bedroom. She pretended to be reading.

Susie came into the room and sat on her bed. "Hi," she said. Gloria was about to reply when her sister spotted the cut on her face and yelled, "How did you get that cut? Gosh, that looks really bad!"

Gloria said, "I ran into a post on the way out to the bus at school."

Susie yelled for George, who was considered the expert on such things for the two girls. "George!" Susie yelled, "Gloria's got a big fat cut on her eye!"

George walked into the room and asked, "What are you carrying on about? I am trying to get my homework done!" When Susie pointed to Gloria's face, George looked at the girl and asked her, "Who did this to you?"

Gloria began to cry and knew she couldn't lie to Georgie because he knew too much. "Dick was here, Georgie; he hurt me bad, worse than ever." George asked her how bad, and she lifted her dress and showed him what Susie hadn't seen before. Gloria was bruised, bloody, and had teeth marks everywhere her dress covered her small body. George's face reddened with anger and his eyes filled with tears. He pressed

his lips together hard for a few moments, because he couldn't bring himself to speak.

When George could speak once again, he told Susie to follow him. George picked up Gloria and took her into the bathroom. Once there, he ran warm water into the tub. Then he turned and spoke to both of the girls. "I am going to look for Dick; I will be back before Mom gets home. Finish cleaning Gloria up, get some clean clothes on her, and hide these clothes. If Mom comes home before me, don't say anything."

Gloria looked at her brother with her eyes wide and said, "I think he is gone back to where he lives with our father, or he has runaway. He is mean like him now. I want to go and hide, somewhere where he, where they, can't find us ever again." George looked at his little sister; he picked her up and told her that someday they would not have to be scared anymore.

When their mother came home later that night, George felt that he had to tell his mother what had happened. When he told his mother about the cuts, bruises, and bite marks, Sylvia jumped up from her seat on the couch. She was going to have to tell Bud about this so that Dick did not come near the girls again. It broke her heart to think that she had raised Dick and that he had become as mean and vicious as his father was.

After Sylvia calmed down, she crept into the girls' room. She lifted the sheet off Gloria's small body and began to sob at the sight of bite marks on the inside of her thighs and small breast. Quickly, she put her fist to her mouth, covered her daughter, and ran to her room.

Sylvia sat on her bed, silent sobs racking her body, and she tried not to wake the kids. She was becoming more aware of the magnitude of what her children had lost; she did not know what to say to express to her kids how badly she felt.

{ 41 }

Reform School

In the few months that passed after Dick's visit, things had gotten quiet. Days passed almost as normal as anyone else's. Gloria had recovered from her visible wounds. Now, however, she was not allowed to play with any of the neighbor children. They did not want her around their kids, afraid she might cause them to become victims as well. Gloria retreated into her world of reading books and going to school. The only social interaction she had was at school and with her siblings, Susie, Sharon, and George. She felt dirty and afraid most of the time.

Sometimes, she would go to a neighbor's houses and ask if she could play with her friends. The answer was always no. The parents did not even tell her, they would make her friends come out and tell her. They would say to her, "My mom and dad don't want me to play with you anymore because of what your brother did. It was in all the papers."

Gloria would walk home, very sad. It was not as if she wanted those things to happen to her, but she guessed it was really her fault after all. Everyone seemed to think so. Sometimes, she was still afraid and she had no one to talk to about

it. Other times, she wished she were dead. She felt so much pain inside sometimes that it felt like her chest would burst.

She had hoped that as time passed, it would get easier for her to forget. No one was allowed to talk about what had happened, or at least, no one did. However, as time passed, Gloria found a place that she could exist in the middle. Somewhere, in the middle of all of the fear, pain, and shame, she had found a place of peace with herself. It let her get out of bed each day and do what she needed to do.

Then came the day when the police showed up at their door again. Gloria feared that the peace was over again and shame grew in her heart.

The Seminole County, Florida Sheriff's car pulled up in front of the house, and two deputies came to the door. Sylvia met them and went outside with them to the patrol car. They had Dick with them and told Sylvia that they had placed him in protective custody.

It seemed that the Brevard County Sheriff's Department had found Dick chained in the backseat of Bud Peterson's car as it sat outside a bar in Titusville. Dick, expelled from school again, had been beaten badly by Bud who then chained him in the car. Rather than feed the boy, they told her, he would throw some bread and water in the car. He would then leave Dick for long hours while he got drunk inside the bar. A call from the bartender, who had tired of listening to Bud brag about his control over the boy, brought officers to the parking lot.

Dick, they said, would do his "business" in the car, which would prompt another beating from his father. The bartender told them that some of the patrons, taking pity on the kid, would hand him food and drink. They told Sylvia he had it rough and thought he would be better off staying with her until his court date in another month.

Sylvia refused to take her son into her home. She explained what had happened during his last visit. She told them how he had hitchhiked to Sanford and assaulted his sister, Gloria, describing the injuries she had suffered. She told them she could not allow him another opportunity to hurt one of his sisters or anyone else. The deputies agreed with her, and when she asked where he would go, they told her he would be in a single cell at the jail until his trial. They said that he would be sent, most likely, to the Okeechobee School for Boys to wait out his sentence. After serving his sentence, he would be released to his parents.

Sylvia told them, as much as she regretted having to do that, she must try to keep her girls safe from him.

That was the only time in the next year that any of them saw Dick. When they drove the long trip to Okeechobee to visit him, he was surly and mean. He scared the girls so badly they refused to return.

Life was changing for the girls; their mom was taking them skating, to the movies, and swimming. There seemed to be more time for fun and lightness than the girls could ever recall. Moreover, there was a new person in their mom's life, and he was very nice. Nevertheless, the girls were wary. Even

though Fred never gave them reason to worry, they would hang back and stare quietly at him. He did not know that the only men that had been nice to them and had not wanted sex from them were a distant memory. Memories, long forgotten, left behind with their "good life" in Indiana.

Their mom continued to work hard and take care of them. Her new male friend was away on ship and would not return for nine months. Sylvia began to look for a new home for them all. If they could leave this house of bad memories, she felt, maybe they could heal from all the bad things that happened.

{ 42 }

Last Year In Hell

In the summer of 1965, Gloria turned ten years old. The family moved from the house on the Old Orlando Highway to a small home closer to town. Neither of the girls' older brothers lived there with them. George had joined the U.S. Air Force after high school, and Dick was still in Okeechobee incarcerated in the reform school there.

Most days were quiet; with their mother working nights, the girls were enjoying the unusual peace and quiet. They were a tight-knit group and got along well for the most part. Two of the girls, Susie and Sharon, had September birthdays. All of the girls were looking forward to the celebration this year.

Their new school, Southside School, was much different from Pine Crest Elementary that they had attended for the past several years. Pine Crest was a new, modern school with open hallways that ran the length of each wing. It also had a modern cafeteria and bathroom facilities.

Southside was an old brick schoolhouse with two stories containing classrooms, offices, and a library. Each classroom had a coatroom at one end and the floors were made of wood,

not concrete. The schoolyard was much smaller than the one at Pine Crest, surrounded by residences on each side. It was a definite change for Gloria who had only attended one school and had younger teachers in her first four years of school.

When fifth grade began in September 1965, Gloria walked into her classroom with anticipation of another year of learning. She had always done well in school, even though she had to complete most of her homework in class or in the library at the school. Gloria's home life had never before been conducive to getting homework done. It seemed that she and her siblings had always been too busy hiding or being tortured in one of their father's training sessions. Now, Gloria believed that she would be able to do her homework without fear or pain getting in her way.

For the first few weeks, everything progressed smoothly. Her teacher, Mrs. Banks, was quite a bit older than the other teachers she had in the past. She seemed nice, but aloof and a bit cold. In fact, she reminded Gloria of her father in one way. Mrs. Banks seemed to be putting on an act that, like Gloria's father, could turn ugly at any moment without any real provocation.

After the initial soft glow of a new school year, tarnished by classmates that talked, did not pay attention, forgot their homework, or generally misbehaved, Mrs. Banks seem to have lost her patience with all of the children.

Mrs. Banks had a paddle in the coatroom and was more than willing to use it. Gloria had never had a teacher who was

so willing to hit a student. There was one boy in class, Ernest, who always appeared to be on the teacher's bad list.

Ernest, it seemed, could never manage to turn in his homework or pay attention in class. The teacher found fault in everything that he did. She often beat him in front of the other students and threatened to take him into the coatroom for a paddling. He was often hurt and cried after the beatings.

The beating served as a warning to the other children in class, and the teacher was able to maintain a quiet class. For most of the students, the class was boring and stressful. The teacher's curriculum was comprised of the memorization facts (state capitals, U.S. Presidents' names, etc.). For math, the memorization of multiplication tables up to twelve was the crowning achievement.

For Gloria, however, the constant threat of being beaten created stress that did not allow her to focus on her work. She was struggling in the environment created by the teacher and often found she was in trouble. The teacher never beat her, but the threat was palpable. In fact, the only student Gloria ever saw her beat was Ernest.

Gloria was struggling in the fifth grade and would often beg her mother to stay home sick, especially when her homework was not complete. However, her mother always saw past the ruse and made her go to school anyway.

{ 43 }

Dick Comes Home

One day, after school, Dick was at the house when the girls arrived home from school. He was alone with their little sister Sharon; their mother had already left for work. The girls were upset; they were told that they would never have to see him again.

Now here he was, sitting in the family room watching television as if he lived there. Susie asked where Sharon was, and he told them that their mother had told her to play in her room until Susie and Gloria got home.

Sharon was in her room, coloring, and looked up and smiled at her sisters when they walked in to check on her. "Can I watch TV?" she asked.

Susie and Gloria sat down next to her on the floor and Susie said, "Let's just stay in here and color for a while."

The first week or two that Dick was home was quiet, as though he was determined to behave himself and not hurt his sisters. He was bored and decided to paint the acoustic tile ceiling block in an alternating blue and white pattern to match the blue concrete block walls. As long as Dick was occupied, the girls would not be worried.

When Dick had completed his painting, he began to show interest in the girls. He would ask the girls to watch television with him or help him clean up after dinner. Sometimes he would ask one girl and not the others. The girls were very wary of Dick and determined not to be alone with him. Because of Dick's history with them, the girls were focusing more on staying out of his way and less on schoolwork. Dick would sit next to one of the girls and try to place his hand in their pants or up their skirts. He would try to talk them into having sex with him. It was not until he forced them, that the girls had to comply in order to remain safe. Susie, twelve, was first since she had been an active participant in the molestation when it had happened before.

One day, on her way to school, Gloria realized that she had forgotten to do her homework. Between all of the tension and terror at home and at school, Gloria was too frightened to go to school. She was walking along a ditch bank that the girls took to school and was so ill at the prospect of facing her teacher and being beaten, that she vomited into the bushes. Gloria took that as a bad sign and returned home to tell her mother that she was too sick to go to school.

She had returned home and she was terrified to find that her mother was not home. Dick told Gloria that their mother had left to take Sharon to Shucksie's house so that she could run some errands before work. Dick pressed Gloria to tell him what was wrong. As he spoke, he slid his hand under her dress. She told him that she was sick and had thrown up on

the way to school. She told him that she was afraid of her teacher and why.

Dick became excited as he listened to Gloria talk about her fear; he continued to press her to tell him more and to allow him to remove her panties. Gloria wriggled and tried to get away from him. Dick looked at Gloria and said, "I promise if you let me touch you, I will take care of that mean teacher."

Gloria replied, "No! I will talk to Mom about her, leave me alone." However, Dick just forced himself on her anyway.

Afterward, Dick dragged Gloria up off the floor, then told her to clean up and put on different clothes. "We are going to your school to talk to that teacher."

Gloria began to beg and plead, "Never mind I did not mean what I said, just let me go to school."

Dick said, "No way am I going to let some teacher get away with hitting my little sister. I will walk you to school."

When the two of them walked into the school, now several hours late, Gloria opened the door to the classroom. When her teacher looked at her, Gloria put her head down and avoided the teacher's angry stare. "Excuse me," Mrs. Banks told Gloria's classmates, "I will be right back." She walked into the hallway where Dick and Gloria stood and asked what was wrong and who Dick was.

Dick told her that he was Gloria's older brother and that Gloria had told him about some of the stuff that was going on in her classroom. Dick told her that she had told him how Mrs. Banks hit one of the students for not turning in homework on time. He also told her that Gloria was not able to

complete her homework for that morning; as a result, he said, "Gloria became so frightened of coming to school that she was physically ill." He told the teacher that he had better never hear that she hit Gloria and that she was not always going to be able to get her homework done on time.

Mrs. Banks replied to Dick and Gloria, "That is too bad. I do not accept late homework assignments. Furthermore, how I run my classroom is none of your business." Dick looked at the teacher. Mrs. Banks grabbed Gloria by the shoulder and started to shove her into the classroom.

As she opened the door, Dick stopped her by slamming his hand against her chest to stop her movement. With the door open, he said to her, "If you lay one hand on my little sister, I will come back and beat you! As a matter of fact, if you do not accept each and every one of her assignments, late or not, I will return one afternoon, and I will fuck you in the ass so hard you will taste my cock in your mouth." Dick said this quietly, but with such intensity, Gloria's eyes opened wide with fear. Looking at her teacher, Gloria could see her teacher was very afraid; she was shaking. Gloria looked at her teacher and shook her head, not knowing what to say.

Dick took Gloria by the hand, and then started to leave, taking her with him. The teacher, as much afraid for Gloria as for herself, took her other hand and told Dick, "She has class to finish today."

Dick said, "I will wait outside for her."

Mrs. Banks told Dick that it was illegal for him to wait in the schoolyard and that someone would call the police if he

loitered there. Dick reluctantly left Gloria there with a warning to the teacher not to hurt his sister or "there will be hell to pay."

Once Dick left the school and Mrs. Banks could see that he was gone, she took Gloria by the hand. Both of them went to the office, and Mrs. Banks asked the school secretary to have someone take over her class. She left Gloria in the outer office and went in to see the principal in his office to discuss what had happened.

Before long, Gloria's sister joined her in the office. They sat silently waiting for something to happen. Eventually, both girls were led into the principal's office. Gloria, asked what her brother had said to her teacher, told the principal what Dick had said and done. She also explained why he brought her to school to talk to her teacher. Susie showed no reaction whatsoever to what Gloria said. The principal told the girls to go sit and wait in the front office until their mother arrived.

As the girls sat and watched, a police officer arrived and went in to talk to the principal and Mrs. Banks. When he came out, he turned to the principal and asked him, "Which one of these girls is Gloria?"

Gloria grabbed Susie's hand tight and started to cry. "Am I in trouble?" she asked.

The police officer knelt down and told her, "No, Gloria, but your brother is in trouble for threatening your teacher." Gloria knew it was bad and she nodded to the police officer. The police officer told her, "When your mother gets here, we will all sit down and talk about what happened."

"Okay," she replied.

Susie was fidgeting about in her seat, anxious to know what Gloria had told the principal. When the adults moved away, she said to Gloria, "Please, please tell me you did not tell them about Dick having sex with us."

Gloria shook her head and told Susie, "When I went home sick, he made me have sex with him, and then he brought me to school and told my teacher he was going to beat her up and do it to her in her butt." Gloria looked up to make sure that no one had overheard, but the look on the secretary's face told Gloria that she had been listening.

The secretary was overwhelmed that a child so young would know about such sexual acts. She was dismayed that the girls seemed to want to keep it a secret. She thought about taking the girls to the nurse's office but decided to place the girls in a conference room until their mother arrived.

When their mother arrived, they directed her to the conference room where the girls had been waiting for her. She sat down and asked the principal to leave them alone for a few moments. When they were alone, Sylvia asked Gloria if Dick had threatened her teacher. Gloria told her mother that he had and it was bad. Sylvia then asked the girls if it was true that their brother was making them have sex with him. Both girls denied that they had said anything like that. Sylvia asked them several times if they were sure, and Gloria finally told her, "I think that they heard wrong when I told Susie what Dick said to my teacher." Sylvia, still not convinced, asked Gloria what her brother had said to her teacher. Gloria reiterated, "He said

that he was going to beat her and have sex with her in her butt if she hurt me." With that, Sylvia was convinced that the girls were telling the truth.

Sylvia told the girls that the police had shown up at the house and arrested Dick. They told her that he would be in jail for a long time for threatening the teacher. She also told the girls that the school had expelled Gloria; they would have to find another place to go to school. It seemed that Gloria's teacher was too afraid to continue to have Gloria in her classroom. Gloria said, "I liked Pine Crest School better." Her mother did not reply; she was not sure how far she would have to move in order to get the girls into a school after this.

The following weeks were busy. Their brother George came home from the Air Force for a visit. Their mother was working and looking for a new place to live. The girls were out of school until their mother could relocate them.

Sylvia eventually decided on an offer to rent a room in a friend's house. The friend's name was Nancy, and her husband was on ship with Fred, Sylvia's fiancé. Sylvia and her girls shared a big room with two beds in it. It was there that they stayed until Fred returned from ship in November 1965 and found a new home on Myrtle Street. The move allowed the girls to return to Pine Crest Elementary School.

One day, without notice, Bud showed up for a visit with the girls. The girls loudly voiced their reluctance to go with their father, but Sylvia told the girls that they had to go. Unenthusiastically, the girls went out and got into the car. Bud

introduced the girls to his new fiancé, Nancy, and her daughter, Christy.

Bud showed no interest in any of the girls. All three of the girls sat silently, staring out the car windows, afraid to do anything else. In an hour, once Bud was satisfied that he had shown Nancy that he had daughters, he returned the girls to their mother. Bud never said goodbye, never said anything in fact, once the introductions were completed. When they arrived back at their home, he told the girls to get out of the car and let their mother know that they were back. Sylvia went out to the car and leaned in the window to say goodbye to Nancy. Bud looked over at her and promised he would send "the next child support payment very soon." Sylvia leaned in a bit farther and told him that she would not expect it at all since she had not received any payments since she left him. She added that the kids were better off without him and that he should not try to see them ever again.

{ 44 }

Dick Sends Help

The evening was winding down. All six children were finished with their chores and were ready to settle down for the night. There had been the usual nightly battle over whose turn it was to wash the dishes after dinner and who was supposed to take out the garbage. Ever since this new family began in December 1965 with the marriage of Sylvia to Fred Voter, a divorced sailor with three children of his own, life had been lively for the group.

They lived together in a blockhouse on Myrtle Street in Sanford, Florida. The house was just down the street from the elementary school where all of the kids, except Sharon who was five, attended school. The house had two bedrooms and an attached "Florida room" that the boys shared. The four girls all shared one bedroom with Sylvia and Fred sharing the other. The house had a very small kitchen off the dining room. The dining room was twice as big as the kitchen with a window that looked out onto a large backyard. As was typical for the area, there was an alley running down the block between the row of houses on their street and the one behind them. There were no fences separating any of the homes on the

block. It was a rental, but it was clean. It was warm in both the winter and the summer, since there was no swamp cooler. It was not much, but it was their first home as a new family. The family lived close to the Naval Air Station in Sanford, Florida; at night, the kids would often lie awake, listening to the loud whine of each Vigilante fighter jet as it would grow closer to the house and roar overhead on its way to some unknown mission.

In the evenings, Sylvia's girls, Susan, Gloria, and Sharon, were required to do their share and get along with the two boys and one girl from Fred's marriage—Freddy, Tony, and Vicky. Four of the children were very close in age—Susan, twelve, Vicky, eleven, Gloria, ten, Freddy, ten, and Tony, eight. Sharon was the youngest at five. There was a lot of arguing and absolutely no favoritism allowed. Both parents were often at work in the evenings, and currently, Fred was away on a tour of duty in the Gulf of Tonkin aboard the aircraft carrier Constellation. He would not return for at least another eight months. Sylvia worked nights as a bartender or waitress and had her hands full keeping track of what the six kids were up to.

Though things were tough from time to time, Sylvia was very happily married to Fred. He was a good man and the Navy life suited her; it certainly offered more security than her first marriage. His children had been raised by his parents after his wife had run off, abandoning them when the oldest was six. They were well behaved and seemed to need the love and attention she gave them. Sylvia and Fred had agreed that the

children should work out their problems between themselves, and they seemed to be managing that very well without killing each other.

From time to time, the kids got into mischief together, jumping off the roof and twisting an ankle, or sneaking into one of the posted lakes in the area. One time, the boys were playing with a gas can and matches. Tony burned his leg when the gas spilled on his pants leg and the pants burst into flames. Overall, they were good kids.

Sylvia was still not sure what had happened to her three girls. She had asked Susan, her oldest girl, a few times without any reply. Both of her older children had left home before she married Fred; her oldest, George was in the Air Force and Dick was in Okeechobee Reform School, again.

None of her kids was talking about what had happened. After the odd comment Gloria made when forced to visit her father the last time, Sylvia had decided against any more visits. Luckily, Bud has not asked. That was not surprising, and Sylvia hadn't kept in touch since there was no chance that he was planning to pay child support, and she was concerned that he might actually harm one of the kids.

On this evening, in their new lives, the kids got ready for bed and settled down to watch television. Susie, Vicky, and Gloria were still in the kitchen cleaning up the dinner mess and making popcorn. Suddenly, there was a knock on the door; Freddy got up and answered the door, closed it, and came back over to the kitchen. He told Susie and Gloria, "There are two guys at the door and they are asking for both

of you." When the girls asked who these people were, Freddy simply replied, "I don't know, they said that Dick sent them." The girls looked at each other, exchanging an odd glance. Since they always did what they were told to do, and even though they were in their pajamas, they headed for the door.

The girls thought that it was strange that Dick would send anyone to see them. Their brother Dick was in reform school again. At least that was the rumor; Mom never told them about such things. Mom never said why when asked, just that she did not know.

When they got to the door, looking through the full-length louvered glass down the center, they could see there were two young men standing at the door waiting for them. Susie opened the door; she and Gloria stared at them and asked them what they wanted. One of the two, a young man about seventeen or eighteen years old, began to tell the girls that their brother Dick had sent them there. He told the girls that both of them had known Dick when they were in Lake Okee-chobee. He told them that their brother had told them that when they got out of the reform school, his two sisters would take care of them. He told both of the boys that Susie and Gloria would let them "lick their pussies and suck their cocks and fuck them both." Both of the girls reacted with shock and fear; they were now sure that their brother was the one who sent these two. They began to scream at the two young men to leave.

Susie, the oldest, had understood the threat more clearly than her younger sister had. After the first few words said by

the young men, Susie has started to close the door between the two groups. The young man who had spoken put his foot in the door and moved his body forward trying to push his way into the house. Susie pushed back and each of the two young men grabbed one of her arms and pulled her out. As they pulled her, Susie screamed out to Gloria, "Lock the door, lock the door!" Gloria locked the door, wanting to help her sister but more afraid of what might happen.

Susie managed to break away and tried to run from the two, heading toward the backyard that was unfenced and offered an escape. Gloria went to the dining room window to make sure that Susie had gotten away.

They caught her before she had gotten far. Both of the men forced Susie to the ground at the back of the house, below the dining room window. The boys forced her to the ground and began their attack. She struggled with one of the boys as he first tried to pull and then just tore off her pajama pants in his excitement. He forced her legs apart and as she screamed, he forced his penis between her legs and inside of her. Gloria had watched from the dining room window as he tore Susie's pajamas from her and began to rape her. He was excited but was having trouble controlling Susie and slapped her across the face to get her to stop fighting. He pushed her legs up above her head and forced his penis into her. Once he was finished, Susie tried to get up, but he forced her back down to the ground and held her to the ground by her shoulders. Gloria could not watch any longer. She sank from the window to the floor. She could hear Susie's cries as they forced themselves

on her; it became more than Gloria could bear. His friend climbed on top of Susie and forced himself on her but could not finish and forced his penis into Susie's mouth. He grunted and grabbed her by the hair as he slammed into her, telling her if she bit him, he would break her teeth. Gloria could hear her sister gagging and crying as he slammed his penis into her mouth repeatedly. When it was over, his friend, excited by the violence he saw, went after Susie once again. Once they had both finished, they told Susie not to call the police. If she did, they said, they would find Dick, and they would all come back for more, and get that little sister next time.

Gloria realized that her new stepsister, Vicky, was saying something to her, but Gloria could not make any sense out of it. She just sat there silently waiting for it to be over. Finally, when she could move, Gloria got up and went into the closet in the bedroom that all four of the girls shared. She lay on the floor and cried for her sister and herself, wondering if they would ever be safe. It seemed that their father and brother proved repeatedly that they had power over them. Even from somewhere else. The sense of powerlessness overwhelmed Gloria. She stopped feeling or crying, there was no use, there would be no help.

Soon, Susie joined her sister in the closet and they spent the night crying and holding each other. Susie was naked except for her robe, and she hurt in so many places from the rape and the hitting. She was so worried that Gloria would tell. She did not want anyone to know, she was so ashamed. She only wanted to make sure that they would not hurt Gloria or Sha-

ron. She was okay; it was not as if that had not happened to her before, and she was twelve after all.

ABOUT THE AUTHOR

Gloria lives with her family in central California's San Joaquin Valley. She works, writes, and is currently attending college to earn her master's degree in creative writing.

To My Readers

Thank you for choosing to read my book. After you have finished reading, I would appreciate it greatly if you would return to the product page on Amazon and leave a review. The link to my book's product page is below-

http://www.amazon.com/Undoing-uncertain-nights-Peterson-children-ebook/dp/B00PUKZHZ8/ref=sr_1_2?s=digital-text&ie=UTF8&qid=1417481491&sr=1-

2&keywords=the+undoing

To be added to my mail list, please send an email to the following address: maillist@biteword.com

To reach me by email directly for any other reason, please email me at this address: notifications@biteword.com

Made in the USA
Monee, IL
14 July 2022

99731549R00167